OHIO RIVER VALLEY EDITION

THE
BOOM
PROJECT

Voices of a Generation

OHIO RIVER VALLEY EDITION

THE
BOOM
PROJECT

Voices of a Generation

Edited by

Kimberly Garts Crum
Bonnie Omer Johnson

ISBN: 978-1-941953-69-3

Printed in the United States of America

Book design by Scott Stortz

Published by:
Butler Books
P.O. Box 7311
Louisville, KY 40257
(502) 897–9393
Fax (502) 897–9797

www.butlerbooks.com

CONTENTS

COMING OF AGE

COMING OF AGING

HOME

ENDINGS

ACKNOWLEDGMENTS

Kimberly Garts Crum and Bonnie Omer Johnson

To begin with, we thank our writers. All have been a pleasure to work with. Their gracious patience and enthusiastic responses have helped us endure the complexity of putting a volume like this together—a complexity we did not fully understand when we began.

Two people who did understand the complexity of this project were our publisher, Carol Butler (Butler Books) and our editor, Susan Lindsey (Savvy Communication LLC). Baby boomers both, their enthusiasm for this collection as well as their clarity, guidance, and competence, have helped us create a beautiful book that will contribute to the literary history of our generation.

Copyediting poetry would have been a dangerous endeavor for prose writers. We thank poet Ellyn Lichvar, editor of *The Louisville Review*, the Spalding MFA program's literary journal, for taking a look at all of the poetry. And we will always be grateful to the Spalding University MFA in Writing low-residency program for guiding us as we learned to craft our stories in our middle years. Without Spalding, we would not have met or guessed that we could pull off this project.

Our focus has been on writers who have lived in cities and towns along the Ohio River. We plan to travel alongside the Ohio River, as explorers of the modern era, to meet our writers, readers, and storytellers. Thanks to graphic designer and Old Louisville friend, Susan Coleman Layman—also a baby boomer—for designing a remarkable logo. We especially love the way she incorporated the river and the infinity symbol.

Kudos to Colleen McCormick, our editorial assistant and a member of the millennial generation, whose literate readings on our three-person review panel helped us identify pieces that were relevant and relatable to a wide audience. Colleen said, "The lessons and experiences the authors narrate resonated with me on an emotional level as I was able to draw many comparisons and parallels to my own experiences. I felt the divide between the baby boomer and millennial generations start to disappear."

Thanks in advance to the bookstores and public libraries, historical societies, civic groups and book clubs, writing support groups, literary organizations, public radio stations, and MFA programs that will welcome the coeditors and contributors for speeches, readings, and conversations.

And to our husbands and children (and Bonnie's grandchildren), we are abundantly grateful. Your interest in, and genuine efforts to understand our need to create this book, buoys us. We have journeyed many decades with John Crum and Steve Johnson, with whom we chose to grow old for better or worse, though the reality seemed remote. Yet, here we are.

INTRODUCTION

Kimberly Garts Crum

"Boom: A loud deep resonant sound as of a distant explosion, breaking surf, a bass drum, etc.; a hum or buzz; the cry of the bittern."
—*Shorter Oxford English Dictionary* (5th Edition)

Within these pages, you will find writing that is provocative, lush, witty, accessible, and universal. Here, writers of the baby boom generation speak on a variety of topics—the river, home, cultural events, coming of age, and the coming of aging. What began as a bucket list item has evolved into an anthology of stories, essays, and poems by people born between 1946 and 1964, and who have lived or are living now near the Ohio River. You will find writers who are indigenous and immigrant Americans; African, European, and Asian Americans; people with acquired and congenital disabilities; and LGBTQ persons. All the writers in this volume tell the human story in unique voices. Some have extensive publishing histories; for others, this is their first publication. All speak in voices that resound.

This book started with a complaint. Two boomers fretted that literary journals request writing that is edgy, fresh, experimental, and modern. We are not fresh, edgy, or experimental. And we are not modern, unless you consider the term "mid-century modern," a unique design grown precious by its age and making a big comeback.

And so, our project began. We invited members of our generation to submit original work through libraries, writing programs, bookstores, literary organizations, and the Internet in the six states along the Ohio River. We chose the river because of its significance in the growth of our nation and its power as a metaphor. The Monongahela marries the Allegheny to form the Ohio River at Pittsburgh, then travels slowly to empty itself into the Mississippi at Cairo, Illinois, on its journey to the Atlantic.

We have learned so much in the work of assembling this book. Namely, the baby boom generation is not one thing. Some of us did not come of age until the 1980s. Not all of us remember where we were when President Kennedy or Bobby Kennedy or Martin Luther King Jr. were assassinated. We don't all remember the Kent State shooting or the Mai Lai massacre or the 1968 Democratic convention or the Chicago Seven or the moon landing or Nixon's resignation. We don't all remember the Birmingham church bombing or the bus boycotts or the integration of Little Rock High School. Some of us remember the days before *Roe vs. Wade*—the whisperings about girls alleged to be pregnant taking six-month absences or going off to New York City for an unscheduled vacation. Some of us remember the Vietnam war; others choose to bury it. Some of us were too young to protest on the streets. At least one of us wore a nickel-plated POW bracelet, to rebel against her parents' support of the war, until her wrist turned green and the bracelet broke in half.

Our generation is pedal pushers, crop-tops, bell bottoms, tie-dye, and leisure suits. We are acid-washed jeans, shoulder pads, and big hair. We are wait until marriage; make love, not war; and cohabitation. We are *The Total Woman, The Feminine Mystique,* and *The Joy of Sex.* We are not a single sound track. We are "Treat Her Like a Lady" and "I Am Woman Hear Me Roar." Coeditor Bonnie still swoons when she hears Pat Boone sing "Love Letters in the Sand." I prefer Led Zeppelin's "Whole Lotta Love."

We are different in most ways but similar in some. We are digital immigrants, haltingly fluent in computer communication, which makes this book, collected and assembled electronically, something remarkable. This boomer remembers operating a mimeograph machine and cutting and pasting college papers with Scotch tape. Who knew computers would revolutionize production, making our efforts easier, but infinitely more complex?

Another thing we boomers have in common is curiosity—a need to explore and understand. Poet and humorist Dorothy Parker said, "Curiosity is the cure for boredom. There is no cure for curiosity."

What you will find here are more questions than answers, more searching than certainty. Though many stories and poems are set in times some readers might consider historical, each is relatable to anyone who has ever searched for identity, connections, and a place to call home.

THE RIVER

Bonnie Omer Johnson

Travel along the Ohio River Valley, 981 miles beginning at its conflux with the Allegheny and Monongahela Rivers in Pittsburgh, Pennsylvania. Before the Cherokee settled in Appalachia, before the Civil Rights Act, JFK, Vietnam, rock and roll, before Neil Armstrong took the first "one small step for man" on the moon and Twiggy was the top model, before color television and air conditioning, there was the Ohio River.

Before Barbie dolls, NASCAR, and climate change, dog boutiques, SUVs, the *Challenger*, Homeland Security, the Super Bowl, Watergate, disco, the digital age, and blatant consumerism, was the Ohio.

Before the Steelers, Kaufman's, Three Rivers' Stadium, three Super Bowl victories, Mattress Factory, the 1979 World Series, the Steel Tower, Pamela's Diner, Buhl's, Keeler's, Allegheny Planetariums, and the Pennsylvania Railroad, there was the Ohio.

Before the 1930s' gangster "Pretty Boy" Floyd met his demise in what was once the Pottery Capital of the World—East Liverpool on the north side of the river—and before "Potter Pete" became the mascot of East Liverpool High School (where Notre Dame's ESPN broadcaster Lou Holtz graduated), and before the Elm Grove Business Association began lunch meetings the second Tuesday of the month, the Ohio River flowed.

Before Wheeling Island became the most populated island in the Ohio River and before the Kruger Street Toy and Train Museum began hosting the annual National Marx Convention in 1998, there was in Wheeling an annual Polka Festival, weddings, skiing, snowboarding, and a weekend called Scrapbooking Paradise.

Before the ferry ran between Sistersville, West Virginia, to Fly, Ohio . . . the river ran.

In Parkersburg, before Brookmar, there was the river.

Before Collis Huntington built the Chesapeake and Ohio Railroad, before wind blew the glass out of the Prichard Building, and before the football team of Marshall University perished in a tragic plane crash, the Ohio River's halfway point was marked in Huntington, West Virginia.

Before 2,000 years of history was painted on Portsmouth's flood wall and before Boneyfiddle was declared an official historic district, the Ohio wound through the land and headed to Maysville, home of the National Underground Railroad Museum.

Before Fiona the hippopotamus became an ambassador for the Cincinnati Zoo, when Pete Rose posters hung in female college dorm rooms across America, and before the Big Pig Gig, the Ohio River connected the City of Seven Hills to Covington, Kentucky.

A southwest turn of the Ohio River leads past Big Bone Lick and General Butler State Parks. Before the town of Goshen was named after the biblical city and became the site of a wildlife sanctuary, the river flowed toward Louisville and fossil beds at the Falls of the Ohio.

Before ESPN showed up to film Vietnam-era Chinook helicopter engines propel hydroplanes spewing rooster tails on the Ohio, before the Madison Main Street Program began holding Girls' Weekends to promote sisterhood and local businesses, and before steamboat captains got liquored up on Kentucky moonshine and challenged each other to races on the Ohio at 10 miles an hour, people of Madison knew the river was its biggest asset. Before Madison was named a historically creative community and a new bridge was scooted onto old pilings, the river nourished economic prosperity and loyal citizens in Madison.

Louisville is currently my adopted hometown, so I can tell you about its nurturing literary community, its excellent fine arts offerings, its excellent universities: Bellarmine University, Spalding University, and the University of Louisville. I can suggest you eat at Jack Fry's, Mike Linning's, or Chef Edward Lee's 610 Magnolia, but did you know Louisville claims it is also the birthplace of the cheeseburger? You know of the Kentucky Derby—run the first Saturday in May since 1875. You might not know the winner of that first derby was trained by future Hall of Famer Ansel Williamson and jockey Oliver Lewis, both African Americans. Seventy-two years before Aristides won the first Kentucky Derby, Lewis and Clark began their westward expedition where Louisville is now situated.

The Ohio River was well known as a commercial avenue for slave traders, but it also had a significant impact on the abolitionist movement. Even as a young lawyer, Abraham Lincoln, for example, born to non-slaveowners, noticed flatboats on the river transporting people tied or chained to the deck.

Years later, after the repeal of the Missouri Compromise opened territories to slavery, Lincoln wrote to his lifelong friend Joshua Speed who favored slavery for its economic contributions. The letter stands as an example of civil discourse between men with strong but differing opinions: "In 1841, you and I had together a tedious low-water trip, on a Steam Boat from Louisville to St. Louis. You may remember, as I well do, that from Louisville to the mouth of the Ohio, there were, on board, ten or a dozen slaves, shackled together with irons. That sight was a continued torment to me; and I see something like it every time I touch the Ohio . . ."

Directly across the river from Louisville are New Albany, known as Gateway to the South, Jeffersonville and Clarksville, Indiana, and the site of the Falls of the Ohio and the Ohio River National Wildlife Conservation Area.

Follow the inlets and outlets, twists and bends, of the 10th longest river in the world, and come upon Brandenburg, populated for more than 10,000 years by Native Americans, most likely Cherokee and Shawnee, verified by the abundance of arrowheads and other artifacts found in the area and rapidly bought up by collectors. Along the Ohio River Valley lived other indigenous peoples in smaller groups: the Mingo, Wyandotte, Delaware, and Cayuga. They preceded the white settlers. The river preceded them all.

Farther down the Ohio are Cannelton and Tell City, Indiana, where an annual Schweitzer Fest every August commemorates the legend of William Tell with a weeklong festival of carnival rides, a soap box derby, an arts and crafts fair, a community-wide talent show, sports tournaments, beauty pageants, performance races, and class reunions.

Across the river from Tell City are Hawesville and Lewisport, Kentucky, quaint farm towns where people wave at everyone they meet, where gardens are lush, and people take care of each other, where the *Hancock Clarion* has delivered the local news and sports since 1893. Tugboat captains pushing coal barges toot their horns at people on the banks of the Ohio.

Before Owensboro, where I grew up and return as often as I'm asked, became the Barbeque Capital of the World, before Old Hickory and Moonlite became the best places to eat, before Kentucky Wesleyan College's basketball team won six Division II NCAA National Championships, teenagers took guitars to the river for hootenannies. Before the riverfront was developed and before celebrities Florence Henderson, Darrell Waltrip, and Johnny Depp became household names, the Ohio River offered its own entertainment.

Evansville, Indiana, and Henderson, Kentucky, face each other on opposite sides of the Ohio. Rich in its arts and community involvement, Henderson is filled with churchgoers and hard workers. Its charm lies in beauteous farmlands and good people. Some of my best friends live there. And now, Henderson boasts a Bliss Artisan Pizza and Ice Cream, too. On the Kentucky side of US 41 stands Ellis Park racetrack for Thoroughbred racing and gaming. It opened in 1922; the river was running there long before the horses were.

Before former Mayor Russell Lloyd of Evansville had a major thoroughfare named for him in Vanderburgh County, before sportscaster Mike Blake broke into regular television programming to relay—through tears—the University of Evansville basketball team and coaches, 29 in all, died in a plane crash, and before Marcia Yockey began a 35-year career as a wacky weather woman and became the 100th woman to earn a helicopter pilot's license, the river ran past Evansville like the town was not even there.

Around a few more bends is Shawneetown, Illinois, once known as a place to get a quick marriage license. Before birth control pills and legal abortions, teens "in trouble" found Shawneetown a life preserver. Today, Shawneetown seems forgotten except for those who eloped there. It is remembered by the river.

Union County, Kentucky is 100 percent rural and a microcosm of every ilk of humanity. From Caseyville to Sturgis and Morganfield on the Kentucky side to Cave-in-Rock, Illinois, you'll find some of the smartest, kindest, rowdiest, sweetest, orneriest, and talkative people on the planet. You'll find my people there and you'll find the river. Cave-in-Rock has its own legends of ghosts, outlaws, pirates, counterfeiters, and serial killers, too, but I never met any, though history authenticates many bad hombres. Cave-in-Rock is named for the 55-foot wide cave carved from limestone river bluffs, still the town's main attraction and a safe hideout for scoundrels. In recent years, the area boasts a state park referred to as "God's recreational area."

Before Thomas Jefferson sent General William Clark and Meriwether Lewis on the Corps of Discovery Expedition, before Clark's servant, York, formed a friendship with Sacajawea, the Ohio River showed the way from where they started in Louisville to what would become an industrial center for steamboats and trains. Many years after he made it to the Pacific Ocean, William Clark founded the town of Paducah, naming it after the Paduké Indians.

Before thousands of quilters and over 400 vendors invaded Paducah in April every year, before Paducah was deemed the City of Crafts and Folk Art, before Hooper's Outdoor Center opened to provide fishing gear and kayaks to river sports enthusiasts, before Lower Town was an Arts District, the river whispered.

Paddle on past Mound City, Missouri, and the Loess Bluff National Wildlife Refuge to Cairo (rhymes with pharaoh), Illinois, where the Ohio River empties into the Mississippi. Before Cairo shrunk in population and commerce, it was an important hub for the Union Army during the Civil War. Once a booming port town, Cairo now is a bit under the weather but the town clings to hope, holds it up like an offering . . . or a future. What first brought life to the area still runs deep; we hope Cairo flourishes again.

Our journey ends here so yours can begin.

THE RIVER RUNS
THROUGH US

*"No man ever steps in the same river twice, for
it's not the same river and he's not the same man."*
—Heraclitus

THE BRIDGE

Roger Hart

December 1967. I was 17 and driving the family pickup, a rusted-out Ford with bald tires that had won the "Ugliest Truck" contest at the Gallia County Fair the previous two years. My father leaned against the passenger-side door, his finger tracing a jagged crack in the window. His two-footed driving scared my mother even when he was sober, and that afternoon he'd had more than a few drinks with my Uncle Orville. When Dad learned I was driving home by way of the Silver Bridge instead of going 20 miles up the river to Pomeroy and crossing there, he threatened to jump out of the truck. He believed the bridge would kill him, and he avoided crossing it with the same sense of desperation that drove many 18-year-olds to avoid the draft and Vietnam.

My father claimed he knew things, that he had a gift. He saw omens and signs, had premonitions, tingles in the bones. He said it was like radar, a heads-up, a "déjà" before the "vu." Bar fights, lightning strikes, flat tires, exploding barbecue grills—he saw them coming before they came, or at least he said he did. He'd predicted the Cincinnati Reds would finish the season more than

10 games out of first place when his buddies at the Little Brown Jug thought they'd win the pennant, and he once warned my mother the clothesline was going to collapse minutes before Monday's wash hit the ground. He said there was no mistaking the gift, although he sometimes ignored the warning or mistook it for an upset stomach caused by spoiled potato salad or a hot dog gone bad.

Squeezed in the front seat of the pickup between my father and me, my mother was thankful to have me behind the wheel, and, despite my father's protests, we were crossing the Silver Bridge.

Nearly two thousand feet long and spanning the murky waters of the Ohio River between Point Pleasant, West Virginia, and Gallipolis, Ohio, the Silver Bridge looked indestructible. The shiny aluminum paint gave the bridge its name and the illusion it was new. Steel suspension cables strung between the two towers reinforced the idea the bridge could withstand anything man or nature threw at it. But first impressions, of bridges and of people, can be deceiving.

My father moaned with each rattle of the suspension cables and clang of the decking, as cars and trucks heading into West Virginia passed in the opposite lane.

"Dying runs in the family," he said, twisting in his seat and checking his door and mine to make sure they were unlocked.

We were high above the Ohio River, stuck in traffic while we waited for the light on the Ohio side to turn green. I wasn't sure why he was so worried. The bridge always popped, groaned, and banged like it was possessed.

"Oh," he said, clutching the dashboard after a particularly hard bump shook the truck.

"Jim!" my mother said.

My mother's "Jim" interrupted his thoughts about dying and he looked around as if trying to find the thread.

"Go on," I said.

The bridge shook again.

My father mumbled, but the bangs and clanks prevented me from hearing him.

"What?" I asked.

A barge loaded with coal slowly passed beneath us. It was a cold December evening, the year Rosemary Masher wore a miniskirt to school and promptly got sent home; the year Tubby Parker, my best friend, painted flowers on the hood of his cousin's VW; the year I first heard the Grateful Dead. The red and green Christmas lights draped across Front Street were barely visible through the coal-stoked brown haze that had settled over the river like a shroud.

"Dying," he said.

I took my eyes off the car stopped in front of us long enough to glance across the front seat. "Dying? What dying?"

"You know," he said.

I did. We were on our way home from the funeral of Aunt Bessie, my father's oldest sister, who had died of a cracked skull after getting kicked by a Holstein heifer. My grandfather and my dad's brother Lou had died four years earlier in a roof fall in Kittany 3, a Foster coal mine across the river in West Virginia. My cousin Bobby, suffering the final stage of Hodgkin's disease, died sitting in a bowling alley while my aunt and uncle argued who could best pick up a 6-10 split. Uncle Roy was leaning against the potbelly stove in his hunting shack on Big Toe Knob when lightning hit the chimney, ran through

Roy and left a six-foot-long melted groove in the linoleum floor. But, as my Aunt Lucy often said, "It wasn't lightning that killed Roy. It was his choking on the plug of Mail Pouch after getting lightning struck." And my cousin Bruce, perhaps the saddest case of all, was poaching deer one cold January night when he bled to death after trying to unzip his coat, forgetting he held his razor-sharp skinning knife in his hand.

"This bridge," my father said.

My mother pressed her hand to her breast, unaware of the tumor growing beneath her fingers, and said *pshaw*, not a word so much as a sound of disapproval. She shook her head slightly to let me know I had nothing to worry about. Other than her deep Baptist convictions, she didn't buy into threats of death, curses, the supernatural, or the mysterious Mothman sightings that had occurred over the previous few years. She called my father's idea that the bridge was going to kill him "utter nonsense."

My father, a cautious man in most matters, had taken what he thought was the safe route. He avoided the Silver Bridge, the mines, the crazy heifers, lightning storms, and Mail Pouch. He drove up and down the river—Franklin Furnace, South Point, Portsmouth, Peebles, Ripley—a cigarette hanging from the corner of his mouth, one foot on the gas pedal and one foot on the brake, demonstrating for school custodians how Rose Chemical floor wax could make their basketball courts shine. He called himself a chemical salesman, but in truth, he was a storyteller, a man who spun mysteries out of the everyday occurrences around town, and for more than a year he'd been chasing down Mothman sightings he read about in the local paper or overheard at the Smiling Skull Saloon. When he couldn't find a mystery, he invented one.

He'd sit on our back porch Saturday afternoons with a case of Rolling Rock and a sales receipt pad from Rose Chemical and stare at the muddy Ohio churning along the bank at the bottom of the hill, the scene blurred by pollution from the coal plants and the plastic sheets covering the screen windows. Then he'd set his bottle down and write a few words in the notebook he held on his lap, his left hand smearing the letters as fast as he wrote them. After filling up one page, he'd stop, put the pencil down and go back to looking at the river.

"Why'd you stop?" I'd ask.

"Looking for a happy ending," he'd say. "They're hard to find."

The bridge rattled as a lumber truck going south into West Virginia passed in the opposite lane.

"Dad?" I said.

"You believe, don't you?" he asked.

The light at the end of the bridge turned green before I could answer, and we began to move forward.

Later that evening, I sat on the back porch with my father. His feet were on the windowsill, and his toes, poking out of holes in his socks, touched the plastic covering the screens.

"Well?" he said, his bloodshot eyes staring at me.

"Well, what?"

"You believe?"

I knew what he was asking. It wasn't a religious question, one that my mother or Reverend Emerick might ask, but a question of whether or not I believed my father had a gift, or curse, for occasionally seeing the future. My passion was science. Apollo 4 had launched the previous month, putting us one step closer to going to the moon. I believed in cause and effect, math, and Newton's Laws, not in my father's world of Mothman and killer bridges. But I didn't want to disappoint him. I sometimes thought he was joking when he quoted Rod Serling's introduction to *The Twilight Zone*: "There is a fifth dimension beyond that which is known to man," he'd say, tapping the side of his head and adding, "and I get signals from that dimension." Maybe his crazy predictions and chasing Mothman sightings were a way of entertaining my mother and me.

"Well," I said, waiting for him to crack a smile that would suggest he was just kidding.

"Listen," he said. "I know your mother doesn't buy any of it, but you, you can keep an open mind, right?"

I wasn't sure. Maybe it all was a joke and I should go along with it. Before I could think of a safe answer, he sipped his beer and started off in a new direction.

"So tell me," he said, "what will you do, you know, after I'm gone."

"Dad, please." I didn't like talking about this. It was the beer talking. I squirmed and tried to think of an answer, one that would change the subject, take us to talking about Christmas or the Cleveland Browns. "I'll go to your funeral and we'll bury you." I had wanted to sound flip, funny even, but my answer came out too serious, like I thought my father's death was imminent. I started to apologize.

"I won't get buried," he said.

"You want to be cremated?"

"No! I don't want to be grilled and roasted. My body ain't goin' to ever be found."

"Dad, I—"

"Shh, shh," he said, like he might be trying to calm a crying baby. "I need to know your plans. It'll give me peace of mind. You know how your whole life is supposed to flash before your eyes in that last second? I don't want that. When the bridge takes me, and I begin that long fall into the river, I want to see what you're going to be doing in the future."

The sun had set and beyond the plastic-covered windows the world was dark.

"Well," I said, not knowing where to begin. "I'll go to college."

"Yeah, yeah, go on."

"Study science . . ."

"And write stories. You'll get that from me."

"Okay, I'll study physics and write stories."

"Girls?"

"Yeah, I'll study girls, too."

He slapped me on the knee. "Bet you will. I mean you going to get married and . . ."

"Maybe. Sure, I guess. When I find the right one or she finds me. We'll have two big dogs and go fishing somewhere up north every summer. I'll teach." I wasn't at all sure about the getting married or teaching part but thought the quicker we got this over the sooner we could talk about something else.

"This is good," he said. "Stay out of Vietnam. Okay, you'll do that?"

"Sure." Actually, I'd been considering enlisting in the army. Unless I got a scholarship, the GI Bill was the only way I could afford college.

"And when you write your stories, what will you say about me?"

I looked at him, the thick head of black hair growing a little gray around the temples, the hooked, hawk-like nose, the deep-set dark eyes, and the ears that resembled radar dishes.

"That you are, were, a great dad. You came to all my basketball games."

"And your track meets," he said.

"And my track meets."

"Will you say how I tapped into that fifth dimension and had visions?"

I hesitated.

He pulled his feet off the windowsill. "Toes getting cold," he said.

The last time I saw my father he sat with his elbows on the breakfast table, sipping coffee from a cracked cup while reading the *Columbus Dispatch*. His black hair was its usual unruly mess, and his chin carried a dab of toilet paper to stem the blood from a fresh razor cut. After he finished, he folded the paper, stood up, grabbed his hat and coat, and headed toward the door. He was calling on a couple schools down the river and would be home early, in time to pick up a Christmas tree and come to my basketball game.

"Good luck," he said. It was Friday, the 15th of December, and we planned to decorate our tree that weekend.

That evening was cold and overcast with a northerly breeze carrying the odor of rotten eggs from coal-burning power plants and steel plants upstream. Cars and trucks jammed on the bridge bumper-to-bumper. Tailpipes blew small, gray clouds, and cigarette smoke floated out partially cracked windows. The river ran fast and icy cold.

Drivers, impatient to get home to dinner or that night's high school basketball game between the Belpre Blue Devils and the Trimble Tomcats, hunched over their steering wheels and fiddled with their radios as they waited for the light on the Ohio side to turn. Those listening to WWVA out of Wheeling heard Bing Crosby singing "I'm Dreaming of a White Christmas." Those tuned to WPKV listened to a news report that the war in Southeast Asia had spread to Laos. Even with the car windows rolled up against the December chill, everyone heard the bang. A suspension cable went slack. The bridge buckled and rolled. The north tower twisted and, like a giant tree after the final swing of an ax, began to fall.

Shopping bags carrying toy guns, dolls, flannel shirts, eight-track tapes, and transistor radios—Christmas presents that had been on layaway since September—teetered on backseats. Jim McCarthy, feeling the earthquake-like shudder, feared a barge had struck one of the concrete pylons. Lily Rutowski, reapplying lipstick in the mirror, thought she'd bumped the car ahead of her. Myrna Tuck's first reaction was to grab the dinner plates she'd picked up at the pottery across the river, a wedding present for her niece. Dave George, sitting high in the cab of his Mack truck, looked over the tops of cars as they tumbled into the river while his best friend and partner, Leroy Newhouse, cut ZZZs in the sleeper. Joe Brazitis, who had attended his first AA meeting that morning, was about to reach for the carefully wrapped bottle of Jim Beam sitting on the passenger seat of his Buick when he felt a higher power shake the bridge and stop him.

Seldon Cooper, my uncle and a Korean War vet, nursing a cup of coffee at the lunch counter in Isaly's, flinched at the sound of what he thought was a mortar exploding. A West Virginia woman glancing out the window in anticipation of her husband coming home, cried out, "Oh God!" as she watched a young woman, a redhead without a coat, running past trapped cars as the bridge fell like a chain of dominoes behind her. The driver of an Omar

Bakery truck ran down to the river and stared helplessly as a woman trapped in a slowly sinking car pounded on the driver's side window. A television repairman coming out of Dickey's Hardware claimed my father's station wagon, stuck in traffic midway across, caught his attention, not because a pine tree was tied to the roof but because he knew my father refused to drive across the bridge.

My mother and I heard his story and others as we stood by the river, watching the crane pull cars out of the water, but we refused to believe my father had been on the bridge.

"Television repairmen can't be believed," my mother said. Two days later, they pulled his blue Olds out of the river. Suspended from a long cable, it dangled and slowly turned like a giant mechanical fish. No body was inside.

Forty-six people died when the Silver Bridge collapsed. Two were never found. Over 50 years later, I still visit the river every time I return home. I stand and listen to the water gurgle as it flows through the Japanese knotweed that has invaded the banks and try to tap into that hidden dimension my father claimed existed, a dimension, as Rod Serling used to say, of the imagination. I send messages to my dad, tell him that my future, much to my surprise, went pretty much as I had predicted. I didn't go to Vietnam, I became a science teacher, and, yes, I write stories. I tell him that finding the love of my life took quite a few years, but I found her, and we have two giant dogs. I tell him I believe.

The water hisses and burbles along the bank.

Sometimes, I swear he answers.

THE OHIO

Tom Raithel

The master of this river
chugs by in a johnboat.
Jeans and jacket smeared with slime,
he stinks of fish and gasoline,

the stubble on his weathered face
as rough as shoreline brush.
He'll never blink.
The muck-brown eyes have seen it all—

glassy high-rise, hobo shack,
railroad baron, shackled slave,
sewage flows and floating dead.
He spits into the water.

And he tells you, as he draws his knife
and slices through a bait fish,
the wind that sweeps the clearest sky
will also drive the squall,

and even the accomplished eye

can fail to see

the snag beneath the backwater.

Sometimes when the moon bobs up

above the darkened cottonwoods,

you'll see his boat and shadow

putter past the island sandbars,

churning out a wake of oily dreams.

Previously published in *Southern Poetry Review*
and *Dark Leaves, Strange Light* by Tom Raithel

DROWNING

Linda Neal Reising

Well, he sauntered in here on July 4, 1968, exactly. I bet you wonder how I remember the exact date, don't you? Well, I remember it because Billy—he was my boy, my only boy—had died exactly 13 years before, to the day.

He drowned in the Ohio River. We'd gone to Evansville with Buck and his wife and kids. Buck's my brother. Or I should say was my brother. He passed away last April. Anyway, we'd all planned a picnic at Sunset Park in Evansville, and then we were going to watch the fireworks that they always set off over the river so nothing can catch fire.

Me and Agnes, that's Buck's wife, were covering the picnic table with a red plastic cloth that I'd just bought at Foster's. The men were pitching washers under some trees. I remember telling Agnes that that red plastic cover ought to last for years, and it just made picnicking so much more sanitary.

I don't remember who screamed first. Maybe it was Billy. Maybe it was Roger, his cousin, or maybe one of Buck's girls. I just remember running to the river, but Pop—that's what we always called my husband—and Buck were already there ahead of me, tearing off their shoes like mad men and looking out at that old river, trying to see if Billy had his head above water.

Well, they both jumped in. They'd swim and dive, swim and dive, but they never saw a trace of Billy. It was just like the river had swallowed him up. I don't remember anything else about that day, but Agnes told me afterward that I went back to the picnic table and folded up that red plastic cover. She said I kept talking about the potato salad, telling her that we had to get it home and put it in the icebox so we wouldn't get poisoned.

I don't remember any of it. It was three days before some men fishing found Billy's body. What was that you asked? Oh, he was 15. I guess he'll always be 15.

I was already 40 years old when he died. Everyone said I was still young enough to have another baby, but I said, "No, sir! If the Lord had meant for me to have a child, he would've let me keep the one I already had."

We never went on another picnic, neither me nor Pop. That red plastic cloth is still upstairs in my cedar chest. I just couldn't throw it away. People never really recover from such things, I guess.

Pop took it real hard. He blamed himself for a long time because he couldn't find Billy in the water. People were curious, too, asking, "Did he jump in? Did he fall? Was he pushed?" What difference does it make? Dead's dead. Gone's gone. There was no bringing him back. Pop had hoped that Billy would take over the Standard station after high school. Of course, I was hoping he'd go to college someplace close. After Billy was gone, Pop kept saying, "What's going to happen to this place? All this hard work and no one to leave it to."

Now look at me. I've gone clear off the subject, but not really, because you asked when he came, and I said that it was exactly July 4, 1968.

I-64 wasn't quite finished then, and I don't know how he got here. I was surprised to look through the kitchen window and see someone walking into Poseyville, especially on a holiday. I'd been helping Pop out at the station that day because my beauty shop—I called it The Yellow Hat Box—was closed on account of the Fourth. Don't you think that's a pretty name? The Yellow Hat Box. Anyway, as I said before, he just saunters up to the station on foot.

You should've seen what he looked like! I turned to Pop and said, "Hide the cash box and get out a tire tool!" Well, Pop just laughed at me and wiped his greasy hands on his shirt—we'd been eating fried chicken for lunch—and went out to see what this fella wanted. Of course, I followed him outside in case there was trouble.

The stranger wasn't much taller than me, and back then, he was sort of slight built, too. He was carrying an old pack that looked like army surplus and wearing faded fatigues. His hair, and I kid you not, his hair was to the middle of his back. It was sort of wheat-colored and would've looked pretty on a girl. It just parted right down the middle and fell around his face. Where the hair left off, a beard took over. His beard and mustache were just a shade darker. I always noticed things like that since I was a beauty operator. But what I noticed most was his eyes. When I first saw him walk up, I thought he must be right out of college, you know, one of those protestor types. But his eyes were older. They were the bluest eyes I ever did see, but the lines, you know, crow's feet, were too deep for such a young-looking man. So I knew he must've been 10 years older than I'd first figured. Either that, or he'd had one helluva life.

Pop walked right up to him. He was about twice this kid's size, and he says, "What can I do for you?" He put his big old hands on his hips. I had to cover my grin with my hand because Pop couldn't have hurt a flea. One time, I caught him up in a tree behind the station, and I said, "Pop, are you out of your mind? What're you doing up there?"

And he says, "Well, Mom, a baby bird fell out the nest, and I was putting it back."

That tells you the kind of man Pop was, so seeing him act so tough was funnier than all get out.

This stranger kind of shuffled his feet and looked down at the oil spots. Finally, he squinted up at Pop and said in a real soft voice, "Thought maybe you could use some help with those cars." And he pointed to a whole line of cars with pink papers under the wiper blades, just waiting for Pop to get to them. He'd been working alone since Monk Meyer had got on at Whirlpool.

Well, Pop was stuck. He couldn't say there wasn't work to be done. So he looked that fella up and down once or twice and said, "Do you know anything about cars?"

That young man smiled then, and I couldn't believe how nice and white his teeth were. And straight, too. They sure didn't go with the rest of him. "I can take apart a motor and put it back together just like that." He snapped his fingers.

Pop looked at me, and I looked at Pop. We both looked at the stranger. Finally, Pop said, "Okay, I could use some help, but I want that hair cut off or pulled back and under a cap. You get that mop caught in that power equipment, and you won't have a scalp left. I don't want you smoking around the gas pumps either. Do you understand?"

He nodded and smiled again. I said, "We'll put you up over here in one of the apartments next door. We own that building, too." I led him to that gray house that's right across the street. Stu Scheller raised 15 kids in that house, but when he tried to sell it after the last one was grown, not a soul wanted it. Finally, Pop bought it just as a favor to Stu.

It was my idea about the apartments. Of course, we had to add some bathrooms and kitchenettes, but we ended up turning a good profit. Most of the renters were real nice, except for a woman named Clare who lived in apartment B for a few months and moved out without letting us know in advance because she said her bedroom was haunted. Wishful thinking, I say.

Anyway, I took him to apartment C and showed him all around, even though there wasn't much to see. Then, before I left, I asked, "What's your name?"

Well, my land, you'd have thought I'd asked the hardest question in the world the way he hung his head and hemmed and hawed. Finally, he said, "Jim. Jim Stark."

"Well, Jim Stark," I said, "you look hungry. Me and Pop were just eating lunch when you came up. Wash up a little and then come back to the station. I'll save you some fried chicken."

Let me tell you, mister, it didn't take that boy five minutes to wash and get over to this station. He'd even pulled his hair back in a ponytail. Pop gave him a cap that said "Goodyear" across the front, and he stuck his ponytail up inside it. He wore that cap every day for the next 15 years. Or every workday, that is. On his days off, he'd let his hair fly free, and it always looked so clean and shiny. He looked like he should've been in one of those Bible movies like they show on television at Easter.

Anyway, like I was saying, he came back to the station, and I brought out some chicken for him. He ate pretty near a whole one all by himself. Then he went to work. That boy had not been fibbing. I don't know a thing about cars, even after all these years in this place, but Pop said he'd never seen a soul who could tear apart an engine as fast as Jim could. Pop was so proud of him. He was always betting with George Lockwood—he worked at the co-op across the street—that Jim could change a tire in less than a minute. Or that Jim could change wiper blades in 30 seconds. It was a game they played, and George always lost.

Yes, Jim Stark made this station his life. I used to say, "Go out and have fun while you're young. Find a nice girl." But he always said that Pop needed him on weekends, which was true.

He never took an interest in anybody until the fall of '78 or '79. I forget which, but I know it was fall because school was getting ready to start. The high school had just hired a new girl from Fort Wayne to teach English. She was taking over for Mr. Granger who was fired for having whiskey in his thermos. Anyway, she almost burned up her car because she forgot to check her oil, so she stopped by the station first thing.

She was pretty, I'll give her that much. She had nice hair, chestnut colored. She was tall, too, and thin. Grace Wilson said that she heard Paula—that was the teacher's name—had won some beauty contest up north, and she really wanted to be an actress, but after two weeks in Hollywood, she came back home.

Well, when Jim saw her, he fell hard. I could see it in his eyes, and I prayed, "Oh, Lord, don't let him get hurt." I didn't think she'd ever go out with him. Not that he wasn't handsome, mind you, but he just didn't seem like her type. She wore little suits and high-heeled shoes. She didn't look like she'd ever done an honest day's work in her life. Not that teaching isn't honest, but it just isn't real work.

Anyway, I was real surprised when she agreed to go out with Jim. He came into the station, big old grin on his face.

"Mom"—he'd called me Mom from the start—"you'll be happy to know I have a date. Paula's going with me to see a movie in Evansville." I was surprised to hear him say they were going to the movies because he'd told me once that he'd never go see one again. A pack of lies, that's what he called them.

My heart felt like it was sinking. I tried to sound happy for him.

"What are you going to wear? Why don't you let me cut your hair?" When I reached up to touch his hair, he jerked away.

"Now, Mom, you know I can't do without my hair. Don't you remember what happened to Samson?"

"Just a trim, Jim. You don't want Paula to be ashamed to be seen with you, do you?"

He finally agreed to a trim, and as I was combing out his hair, I noticed a big scar on his scalp. Of course, I'd never seen it before because of the hair.

"How'd you get that scar?" I asked him.

At first, he turned a little white around the lips, then he said, "I was in a car wreck when I was a kid."

I wanted to hear the whole story, but I'd learned a long time ago not to push Jim. He told you exactly what he wanted you to know, no more, no less.

"You know, Jim, you'd be a mighty handsome man if you'd let me cut your hair short and give you a shave," I told him.

"Well, Mom, I'd probably be so handsome I'd have to fight off the girls, so it's easier to just be disguised as an old hermit."

I'd never thought of the hair as being a disguise until he said that. At first, it got my mind working. Maybe he was on the run from the law or something.

But he'd been so good to Pop and me. I never asked to cut his hair again.

He went out with Paula every weekend until Christmas. I could tell that Jim loved her, but he wasn't the type to open up and say so, probably not even to her. Over the holidays, Paula went back to Fort Wayne, and while she was there, she saw a young man she'd known in high school. He'd taken over his daddy's job at the bank. When Paula came back, she was engaged.

It just about killed Jim. The night she told him, I'd been in bed since about 10:30, but around two o'clock, I woke up because I heard someone banging on something down below in the garage. We lived upstairs, you see. How Pop slept through it, I'll never know, but I crawled out of bed and down the back stairs. I went out the door and looked through the window. There was Jim, with a tire tool, pounding the living daylights out of an old roadster he'd planned on rebuilding. He was crying and saying something about how it wasn't fair that he couldn't live a normal life like everyone else. There was something about him that looked so familiar right then. Not like my Jim, mind you, but like someone else I should've known.

He finally calmed down and went to his apartment. He never knew that I'd seen him through the window. After that night, Jim was different. I could tell that he was getting the fever to move on, but he felt like he owed me and Pop. He spent a lot of time by himself, reading and writing something in a little notebook. I tried to sneak a peek, but I never saw what he wrote.

I guess it was about three years after that when the first of you guys showed up. A man named Parker had his Mercedes quit on him. Pop towed him off the interstate and told him that he wasn't very good with foreign cars, but he'd do what he could. That Mr. Parker didn't seem too keen on having Pop mess with his car, but what choice did he have? He made it clear that he didn't want to stay in Poseyville any longer than he had to. I told him that he could stay in one of our apartments until they got the car parts and got him all fixed up.

As I was leading Mr. Parker to his room, he stopped on the steps and started staring at something in the yard.

"Who's that?"

I looked over and saw Jim slouched against a tree with a cigarette dangling from his mouth. He was using a pocketknife to clean his fingernails.

"That's Jim Stark. He works for us. He's the best mechanic in the county, so your car will be safe with him."

"Did you say Jim Stark?"

"Yeah, why?"

"Don't you know who Jim Stark is or was?" He was getting kind of excited, and I was scared to ask. In the back of my mind, I was always afraid I'd walk into the post office and see Jim's picture on the wall.

"That was the name of the main character in *Rebel without a Cause*."

He kept looking at me like I should know what in the world he was talking about. "James Dean? *Rebel without a Cause*? You never saw it?" He was sweating now, and he got a little notebook out of his suit coat and started writing something down.

I asked him what he was doing, and that's when he told me that he was with *The Gossiper*. I'd seen those papers in the grocery store, but I'd never read one, mind you, except when I was waiting to be checked out and the line was long. I did recall reading the headline about aliens stealing President Kennedy's body, and I remembered seeing a picture of a three-headed baby once.

Well, Mr. Parker wasn't in any hurry to leave after he saw Jim. He kept following him around and asking him questions. Of course, Jim never answered any of them. But once he lost his temper and grabbed Parker by the front of his shirt and was just getting ready to sock him a good one when I came around the corner. I screamed, and Jim let him go. Maybe I should've let Jim hit him. He deserved it. But I didn't want Jim getting into trouble with the law. I finally talked Mr. Parker into going for a ride with me out to Pete Schmitt's farm. He had some Holsteins that had strange markings on their bodies, the shapes of Mickey Mouse and Donald Duck, I think. You had to look awful close to figure them out, but at least I kept that Parker fella away from Jim.

It was two or three days before Mr. Parker's Mercedes was as good as new. Pop and Jim worked 12 hours a day to get it done, just so they could be rid of him. He swore as he got ready to leave that he'd be back. But just as he was pulling out, Jim went to his car window and leaned inside. I don't know what he said, but Mr. Parker turned white and squealed his tires as he pulled out of here. We never saw him again. But I guess he must've told someone because you're the fourth—or fifth—reporter who's been here in the past year or two.

Like I told you when you first came up, Jim left here over a year ago now. Pop had a stroke not too long after Mr. Parker stopped by. Jim stayed here and helped me run the station. I'd stopped fixing hair a long time before when my arthritis got bad. But then Pop died a few months later, and I thought it was time to close the garage for good. I tried to get Jim to stay and help me run the apartments, but he was ready to move on.

I'd forgotten how long he'd been with us until he got ready to leave. Then I noticed how much gray his old beard had in it, and his eyes had a lot more wrinkles around them. And I tell you I cried after he was gone. It was just like when I lost Billy. I never cried at first, not when he left, but later I cried until

I thought my heart was going to bust.

After he left, I went up to clean his apartment. All those years, I don't think I'd ever been up there. It looked just the same as the day I took him up there and asked him his name 15 years before. It was like he'd never really lived there. The only thing he'd left was this book. I know he left it for me. He'd never give it to me straight out. It's a book of poems by James Whitcomb Riley. He was from Indiana, too, you know. This is the same piece of paper he put inside, and he'd circled the title of this one poem called "Away." It's all about how when someone's dead, he's not really gone. He's just away.

Do I think Jim Stark was really James Dean? You see, I guess what I've been trying to tell you is that I don't know who he really was. And I don't care. That's something you'll learn when you're as old as me. It's not who you are that's important; it's what you are. But now my Jim is gone. Swallowed up. There's more than one way to drown.

LOVE, LIFE, AND THE BELLE OF LOUISVILLE

Yvonne Vissing

The best summer job I ever had was selling hotdogs, popcorn, candy, and soda, under the watchful bespectacled Coke-bottle gaze of Miss Ann in the concession stand of the *Belle of Louisville* steamboat. She was widowed, gray-haired, with a grumpy demeanor that masked a heart of gold. She kept us concession girls in line and monitored our interactions to keep us from getting into trouble with the deckhands.

Deckhands were guys. They got to wear uniforms with *Belle of Louisville* patches on their shirts and were always doing something different. One minute they were bringing ice to the concession stand, the next tying the boat's lines to the dock, swabbing the deck, bringing coal to boilers, or chatting with the guys about much more interesting things than popcorn. These muscular, tanned, handsome young lads made regular visits to grab an icy soda and flirt, about which we giggled when they sauntered back to work. We all picked out our favorite guys, and I got pretty sweet on the one with blue eyes and a big flashy smile.

During those long summer days, I did fall in love; I fell in love with the river. I fell in love with paddle wheeler steamboats and learned to guffaw at people who didn't know the difference between gas-run paddle wheelers and actual steamboats. I loved talking with the swarthy fireman who ran the boilers and adjusted the gauges to make the right amount of steam. I loved the engineers, old guys who kept everything running smoothly. We concession girls and deckhands would congregate by the time clock, waiting for one minute past to punch out so we could claim an extra 15 minutes of pay, and no one in the main office ever complained. I loved the opportunity to play chopsticks on the calliope, pressing the tiny keyboard as steam whistled up the pipes to blast noise the whole universe could share. I loved sitting up in the pilot house where it was quiet and calm, cruising down the river with Cap, like we owned it all. I loved the gilded antlers that announced the *Belle* as winner of the Great Steamboat Race. I loved stealing smooches with the blue-eyed deckhand who had keys to the locked captain's quarters. I fell in love with excitement watching crowds board the gangplank while calliope music filled the air. I was in love with the fact that every excursion was a new and different experience. I loved it all.

The *Belle* had a combination of public trips and chartered events. The afternoon public runs went upstream around the islands or downstream through the locks. Tuesdays were teen-hop nights, when rock bands wailed, Saturdays were moonlight cruises, featuring music more suitable for the general public, like Creedence Clearwater Revival's "Rollin' On the River." Everyone came for a good time and fun was contagious. I remember scolding complainers and telling them it was impossible for them to be seasick on the river. Once I tried to speak French to a gentleman from Paris who asked me if he should take candy or flowers to the home he was visiting.

Miss Ann didn't want to work the teen hops, but us younglings did because she wasn't there to watch us. The electric guitars and drums were piercingly loud, the light shows riveting, and the crowd was "a hoot and a holler," as Captain Clarke "Doc" Hawley and purser Roddy Hammet surmised. Doc and Roddy were wonderful, honest, fun, kind, and dapper in their ship administrator uniforms and watched to keep us out of trouble. The *Belle* didn't have a liquor license, but people could bring alcoholic beverages—except on teen-hop nights, where young people simply became stealthier about how to do so. Most teens were busy cruising potential dates, smoking weed, or doing other drugs, as demonstrated by the squinty-eyed guy panicking at the concession stand, trying to find the "tin foil" he lost. Doc and Roddy were quick to intervene when the teens started throwing the life preservers or chairs overboard, or when girls got upset because guys were too pushy.

The moonlight cruises were sedate, but a person we called "The Man" always boarded with a briefcase the deckhands said was filled with bottles of booze, cigs, drugs, or condoms, about which word spread like wildfire. Rides would always end with lovers embracing and looking wistfully at the stars or some pretty tipsy folks groping Ts and As as we pulled into the dock. Deckhands quickly overtook the dirty tables to clean up, but their enthusiasm revolved around seizing money drunks had accidently left on the tables.

Boots, Cap's wife, ran the souvenir shop across the dance floor from the concession stand. She was the buyer, organizer, and seller. She sold *Belle* T-shirts, captain hats, pirate spyglasses, treasure maps, toy fish, and lobster lollypops (there are no lobsters in the Ohio River). But her favorite item was the bell. Boots would shake her bells when the refrain from Chuck Berry's hit song "My Ding-a-Ling" played, and people would clamor to buy them. She smiled and took their money.

Chartered events, where groups rented the boat for special outings, were extra entertaining. Some were predicable, like when schools rented the *Belle* for end-of-the-year celebrations. There were proms with fancy decorations, tuxedoed stallions, and girls with gowns that made parents shudder or go bankrupt. There were always more women than men on senior citizen trips, women dancing breast-to-breast as the band (often a guy squeezing the accordion while a lady plunked the piano) played old favorites that resulted in geriatric flash-mob type sing-alongs. Corporations rented her for their employees and catered awesome (often barbecued chicken) dinners we were invited to share.

But my favorite charters were when the black churches in Louisville rented the *Belle* for Sunday evening cruises. These were fundraisers for the churches and were super fun to work. As people waited in long lines on the dock to board, we ogled at handsome men wearing suits that had style and color— lime green, bright purple, sunshine yellow, neon blue suits with flashy ties over shirts of bright complementary colors that made their skin radiant. Being a pale little white girl, I'd never seen people wear color so beautifully. Gentlemen escorted high-heeled women upstairs and onto the dance floor while big bands with horns played music that made us wiggle our behinds behind the soda dispensers.

In the old days, steamboats would tramp down the river and stop at different ports to take crowds for a ride. No food was sold on these tramps, so no concession staff was needed. But Boots asked me if I'd come to help her cook for the crew on one weeklong jaunt.

We slept on cots in the souvenir store.

"Wake up honey," Boots said as she woke me at two a.m. "Crew changes are at three and they'll be hungry. We have to go cook."

Stumbling downstairs to the galley hatch, we fried bacon and scrambled eggs, brewed coffee, and toasted bread. Boots told me story after story about her life on the boat, tramps she'd made, and characters she'd known.

"Here. You need this," she said, pushing a glass into my hand. She taught me that real river women drink Jack Daniels straight at three a.m.

After crew changes, we cleaned the galley and I took another glass of Jack up to the pilot house and watched the sun come up over the river. Pilots had to memorize every curve of the river to be licensed to operate a boat, even if they navigated only small sections. Each pilot could navigate the entire Ohio River. This was before the days of GPS and computer navigation devices. We and the passengers counted on a good pilot; all were smart, savvy, and calm.

Once I was allowed to ride the *Belle* in the Kentucky Derby Festival Great Steamboat Race against the *Delta Queen*. The *Queen* was a bigger, fancier steam paddle wheeler from Cincinnati. The race course was upstream, around an island, and back under the bridge. The prize was the Golden Antlers and the right to hang them like a masthead. After one race, in which dignitaries crammed on the *Belle* to drink mint juleps, the weight of so many people slowed her down and she lost. After that, invitations were rare. Windows were opened so that there'd be no wind resistance; a lighter, faster boat had a better chance of winning—and usually she did. My favorite race was the year Cap had two tugboats hiding on the back side of the island, so when the *Belle* came steaming toward it, the tugs popped out, zoomed to either side of her, and swung her around so she could make the turn faster and win. While the captain of the *Delta Queen* had a hissy fit, Cap said there was nothing in the rules that forbade the move. Soon afterward, race rules were reevaluated. There was the horrific thought of having paddle wheelers that were not *steam*-operated race, and different boats were invited over the years to keep the race lively. The race continues and while it's different than steamboat races of the old days, it's still fun.

The river is always changing. The current, the boats riding on her, the weather, the crowds on the boat, the conversations, the challenges, the opportunities for laughter, always new, always the same. Transformation is the natural order of life. Things have changed for the *Belle*, and for all of us, since those sweet days on the river. The *Belle* has lived a long life, first as the packet *Idlewild*, morphing into the *Avalon*, and finally the *Belle of Louisville*. The *Belle* is said to hold the record for miles traveled and years operated for a steamboat its size.

Some things do change. Cap and Boots have passed over the Great River, as has Miss Ann. Doc and Roddy moved to New Orleans to work steamboats there. Roddy was murdered in a nonsensical robbery. Doc has established his place in history as a premiere steamboat captain. Deckhands Mike Fitzgerald and Kevin Mullen became captains on the *Belle*. Keith Norrington, who taught Kentucky and Indiana what calliopes sound like, became curator of the Howard Steamboat Museum. And me? After all that people-watching, I became a sociologist. I'm a college professor near water and boats in New England, a researcher and author who is still secretly in love with the *Belle*, the Golden Antlers, and that smiley-faced deckhand.

THE BOOM GENERATION

———✄———

"We fell somewhere between our parents' '30s' idealism and our kids' '80s' cynicism. Somewhere deep down, we still believe that all we need is love, love, love. Somewhere deep down, we question how we got gray hair. How on earth did we get to be the grown-ups?"

—Erica Jong

IN THE EYE
OF THE STORM

Dianne Aprile

A crescent moon, a lilting tune, a prayer that soars above,
Your daughters sing while vistas ring to honor the school we love.

We were three months into our high school careers, just getting to know one another, when the first shoe dropped. Rushing out from PE class on a blustery Friday afternoon, sprinting to English class from the old gym located on one side of the Ursuline campus to the brand-new classroom building on the other, we were stunned to hear the news shouted our way.

The president was shot.

We were Catholic girls, 14 years old, most of us fresh from Louisville's parochial schools, full of dreams, ideals, and the promise of a safe, hopeful world in which to live.

And why not? Our church had recently flung open its windows, in the words of its spiritual leader, to welcome the winds of change. Our nation had laid to rest a longstanding religious barrier and elected a young Catholic man to its highest office. Our new school was giving us the first glimpse of what women could do on their own—run a school, the whole shebang, from superintendent and principal to calculus teacher, basketball coach, and science-club moderator. Here at Sacred Heart Academy, our class officers, star athletes, chemistry-class whiz kids, and state-champ debaters were all—get this—girls.

Everything was possible.

Then came the assassination of the president, the first challenge to our optimism and a sign that the world beyond our woodsy Lexington Road campus was not as peaceful as we imagined.

By the time we graduated in 1967, the whole world seemed to be in the throes of an adolescent identity crisis not so different from our own. The chaos we felt within ourselves as teenagers seemed to echo the turmoil in our culture, in our church, and in the role young women were expected to play within both. Though we were too busy growing up to notice it, the rules we had started out with no longer applied.

By that day in May when we traded our threadbare uniforms for white caps and gowns, the Beatles' claim to greater popularity than Jesus no longer seemed shocking. Nuns and priests were leaving their religious orders in record numbers. The Pill was routinely stocked on drugstore shelves. The women's movement was bursting through the all-male doorways of Harvard, Yale, Cornell. The Summer of Love was about to begin.

And the Vietnam War, for so long just another clipping in current-events class, was as real as the boy next door.

Dear Sacred Heart, school of my heart, lovely the virtues that set you apart.

I took a video camera to my 20th high school reunion, a sunny weekend in 1987. The idea of taping my old classmates, live and in color, as they reminisced about the agony and ecstasy of Catholic girls' education in the swinging '60s, and then playing it back again and again on a television screen—well, it was an image I couldn't resist.

After all, this coming together of girlhood chums was about change, right?

About the evolution from our adolescence, which most of us Catholic schoolgirls experienced as one long exercise in delayed gratification, to our middle age in a decade whose trademark very well could be the VCR, and what we thought then was the most immediate of gratifications, the instant replay.

So I took the video camera to the country club luncheon and trained it on 38-year-old women who, despite the gray hairs and the lines around the eyes, still seemed 16 to me. I asked them questions. They gave me answers.

Later, back home, I replayed the 20 minutes of jumpy videotape for myself and a former classmate who lives in Chicago. We hooted at the stories people told and marveled at the way so many personalities seemed untouched by time.

But one image stood out.

It is a close-up of someone from our freshman homeroom, someone who had moved out of town after college, answering my question about what she remembers most from our first year of high school.

"Laughter," she says. "Fun."

She glances away for a second, and you wonder, "What's she thinking about?" Then she looks back at the camera and with a bemused, almost wistful expression, says, "I'd like to go back."

I remember the laughter, too. But I also remember other things. Like friendships so intense they hurt, so special I thought they would last forever, and which—granted, in a different way than I expected—have.

Still, I'm not sure I would want to go back. Even for a moment. I like the memory as it sits in my mind today: a picture grown fuzzy with age, the disappointments and awkwardness of adolescence worn smooth by the passage of time. We talked about that at the reunion. At a 10-year reunion, you're just getting started in life, still proving yourself, eager to present a successful image that will erase the insecurities of the past. But 20 years give you perspective. The worst memories of adolescence fade, while the best move into sharper focus.

It hasn't always been that way.

There was a time when I looked back and regretted having spent four years in an all-girls school, stuck in an unflattering uniform, socially blockaded from the opposite sex, instructed by women who lived together in a locked-up wing of the school that was off-limits to students.

This was about the same time I thought my mother was ridiculous for devoting herself to raising my brothers and me, enjoying our successes and mourning our losses vicariously.

Eventually, I recovered from both notions.

A friend I worked with once told me she used to look at Catholic girls as they walked home from school together in their look-alike uniforms and think sadly of how they were being stripped of their individuality, forced to conform. But I look at those blue-and-white outfits today as a noble effort to minimize the differences between girls who could afford to dress in the latest fashions and those who couldn't. Besides, how were our uniforms of oxford cloth and wool so different from the ones of madras and chino that reigned supreme at coed schools?

And isn't learning to look beneath the surface for one's individuality, beyond clothes and cars, a major part of the work of being a teenager?

For us you've striven, to us you've given, courage and joy and our shining start.

Sacred Heart had an academic-track system in those days, and I began as a freshman in a group known, politically incorrectly, as the "top class." We spent our first year together in homeroom 309, under the tutelage of Sister Mary Olga, and for the most part, we ended up in the same classes year after year. That was only one of the things I'd change if I could go back in time and Photoshop my past. Also, the lack of any girls of color. That wasn't happening anywhere in or around Louisville, Kentucky, in those days. Still, it's a fault line in my education.

Despite the school's despised nickname, Snob Hill Academy, we were solidly middle-class kids who hailed from a mix of old city neighborhoods and newer suburbs in Eastern Jefferson County.

Sister Olga loved Peanuts cartoons and us, even after the day we were threatened with expulsion for passing around a primitive questionnaire known as the "purity test," designed to measure our sexual expertise. I remember having to have some of the questions explained to me. Embarrassing, but I was not alone in a lack of knowledge in this category of social life. It was the '60s all right, but it was also Kentucky.

The expectations for our homeroom were high; the standards nearly inflexible; the pressures ever present. Like siblings in a big family, we were intensely loyal to one another but competed like crazy. Before each test, we prayed to heaven for guidance. Then fought like hell to outscore each other.

What I did not value until much later was the social experience. In my 20s, the oddity of an all-girls Catholic education was something to rebel from, to joke about, to reserve for shock value or comic relief. We had to take ballet freshman year, for pity's sake, and if our hemlines didn't touch the floor when we were asked to kneel for a spot check, we were in big trouble.

Everybody's heard the stereotypes of nun-run Catholic education. The hilarious stories of straitlaced sisters warning impressionable girls about the dangers of patent leather shoes reflecting up. Or the horror tales of rulers wielded in the name of God.

In reality, I was taught by Ursuline sisters for 12 years, and I cannot recall a single mention of shoes—other than a suggestion that our well-worn loafers could use a shine. And no one ever raised a hand to me. I'm afraid the image I carry with me today has little in common with Sister Mary Ignatius, the fanatical nun caricature in Christopher Durang's satire about growing up Catholic. Yet I suspect my recollection is, in its own way, as oversimplified and one-dimensional as the playwright's.

What I remember are women who were well-educated, self-confident, strong-willed individuals. Dedicated career women. They belonged to a woman's association that had been around since the 1500s, the first Catholic order established for the purpose of educating young women. Unlike most of our mothers, the nuns did not depend on husbands—or men, for the most part—financially or socially. Instead of chasing after children, they spent their summers working on advanced degrees, writing papers, doing research at faraway campuses.

How many other teenage girls, in the mid-'60s, had that kind of role model?

Their motto was simple: "Those who instruct many unto justice shall shine as stars for all eternity."

Some took that promise more seriously than others. One of my favorite memories is the time our plucky government teacher led a group of us downtown, placards in hand, to march in favor of a controversial open-housing ordinance before the board of aldermen.

Another special teacher taught a few of us a creative-writing course one summer. I can remember sitting on the school lawn every morning for weeks, we girls in our Bermuda shorts and round-collared blouses and Sister in her black-and-white habit, all of us writing our hearts out.

Both these women left the order before I finished college—an indication, I suppose, that their lives were not as fulfilling as I wished to believe.

Other nuns remained in the order. They took back their real names, put on regular clothes, moved away, changed jobs. At the reunion, someone reported that our senior English teacher, a bright, posed, open-minded nun who expected and inspired our best, was in Guatemala, training for her stint as a Witness for Peace in Nicaragua.

I wasn't surprised to hear it. What she taught us was to think for ourselves, to ask questions, to speak out.

Most of our teachers were nuns—but not all. There were other women on the faculty, some married, some mothers, some not. The best of them, like the biology teacher who was still there three decades after I graduated, taught us the joy that comes with accomplishment. While I was there, the only men were a handful of priests who came in from their parishes to lecture in religion classes once a week.

Of course, you could argue that what we received in the way of early feminist training was more than offset by the absence of the opposite sex.

School rules banned boys from even picking us up in the parking lot after school. Certainly we mourned not having them around at times, particularly when our school dances rolled around, and we found ourselves in short supply of guys to invite.

But on a day-to-day basis, it was no big deal. Like wearing uniforms, the absence of boys was eventually accepted as a convenience. One less thing to worry about. One less distraction. Not that we weren't as obsessed as any other group of adolescent girls.

It is just that in the classroom or on the basketball court, we were never tempted to defer to boys as keener intellects or superior athletes. I recall, years later, finding it humorous when girls' athletics made the big time in coed schools. It took a federal law to put it on a par with boys' sports.

It's true I missed out on the possibility of developing good, close, non-romantic friendships with boys in high school because I wasn't hanging out with them day to day. And true, I didn't learn to compete with them, *mano a womano*. But in the '60s, that was hardly what the "real world" was about anyway. It takes a long time to get close to equality, baby. I'm still waiting.

Today, in a society where women can and do compete daily with men (albeit on an uneven playing field), you could argue that single-sex education is an anachronism, a throwback, an artifact from a best-forgotten era. Or you could ask yourself, "What's wrong with first learning what you can do on your own, then tackling the 'real world' armed with that knowledge?"

Loving you so, onward we go, Setting the hearth fires and tapers aglow.

It happened so long ago it feels like a different universe, a different set of rules. The hockey games at Seneca Park. The Sunday night mixers in the Trinity High School cafeteria. The term papers. The proms. The graduation parties.

51

At our 20th reunion, what we learned had happened in the course of the previous 20 years is what you would expect: part triumph, part tragedy. Lots of children, lots of divorces, lots of remarriages. In different ways, we each made peace with our common religious background. The place where I've settled is far from where I started out in terms of religious geography, though I guess you never leave your hometown totally behind. That's especially true if it was through learning the lay of the land there that you cultivated your own internal landscape of ethics and values.

Unlike classes before ours, the Class of 1967 did not produce an Ursuline sister, a sign of the times more than a repudiation of the individuals we knew. The class of 198 women did produce a child psychiatrist, a fertility specialist, a college financial administrator, a psychologist, an opera singer, a caterer, a dental hygienist, a flight instructor, several lawyers, small-business owners, social workers, nursing directors, landscape designers, secretaries, artists, and teachers of every stripe. And an abundance of homemakers.

At that reunion, two women showed up pregnant, one for the first time. One extremely fit-looking woman showed off a portrait of her five sons—the oldest 19, the youngest a toddler of two. Some had no children, either by choice or by fate. And one arrived wearing the old uniform, a sight that made us all smile.

But details like these don't begin to tell the stories of people's lives. A carload of doctorates does not a successful class make. Nor do hordes of children or bundles of money. We all knew, as we glanced around the sun-drenched room at the glinting jewelry and chic outfits, that the worst pain and the greatest joy often don't show on the surface.

We learned that long ago, as schoolgirls, struggling awkwardly to find the deeper meaning beneath the surface of a poem, a friendship, an assassination.

Not long after we left Sacred Heart, one of our classmates died in a car accident. I still think of Diane the way she looks in her senior picture— blonde, pretty, big smile. Her mother called me a little while before our 20th reunion, asking if I'd take some pictures for her.

She said she wanted to see what we looked like today, how we had changed.

I've been to several reunions since then, including the big 5-0 in 2017, and each time I think of Diane and our first glimpse of mortality as a group of women on the brink of a new era.

Fling we our colors to brighten the sky, daring to try, hearts beating high.

We shall remember and love you, we vow, ever as now, dear Sacred Heart.

Maggie and Jackie came to my house the day after the 20th reunion. We ordered in pizza and, over beer and Cokes, picked through boxes of dusty photographs, old student handbooks, and wrinkled notes passed in some long-forgotten religion or history class.

"Di, I'm kind of mixed up! I feel awful! . . . Call me tonight."

A rusty French Club pin, a yellowed tassel, a term paper analyzing the women characters of Tennessee Williams. A senior-prom dance card with a tiny white pencil dangling on a cord, the song title "Almost There" printed in script on the back, "Barefootin'" and "Midnight Hour" scribbled inside.

They were amazed that I kept this stuff. I was amazed they didn't.

Surely they knew then that someday, somewhere, on the floor of somebody's den, we'd be together again, trying to figure out what made those four years in the middle of the 1960s so intense, so memorable.

Was it the secrets we shared? The absence of guys? Our first taste of feminism? The fact that we were somehow different, set apart, a bit of a mystery to our public-school friends? And to ourselves?

Maybe it was simply this: From our protected place in the eye of the storm that was about to touch down and rearrange the world, things looked calm and peaceful.

Who wouldn't cherish times like those?

Revised from an essay that originally appeared in *The Things We Don't Forget: Views from Real Life*. Copyright © Dianne Aprile

AS WE SLEEP
IN OUR CRIBS, 1947

Joan E. Bauer

The proceedings of the US Congress are first televised.
The Communists take power in Poland.

Christian Dior introduces the "New Look" in Paris.
Wernher von Braun marries Maria, his first cousin.

Jackie Robinson signs with the Dodgers.
The Cold War begins.

An extraterrestrial vessel is spotted at Roswell.
The *Kon-Tiki* smashes on the reef at Raronia.

As India is partitioned, Muslims chooses the name Pakistan.
The Communists take power in Hungary.

Princess Elizabeth marries at Westminster Abbey.
Meet the Press begins on NBC.

The Iranian Army takes back Azerbaijan.

The HUAC begins investigating Communists in Hollywood.

Cambridge admits women (as full-time students) for the first time.

In a cave near Wadi Qumran, someone finds in pottery jars,

what come to be known as the Dead Sea Scrolls.

Jessica Tandy stars on Broadway as Blanche DuBois.

Previously published in *Uppagus* literary journal

INDEPENDENCE DAY

Diane Cruze

My parents' preparations are monumental as they pack our car with their three children, blankets, food, drinks, fireworks, and folding chairs for an outing to Shawnee Park for a Fourth of July picnic. Our destination is a large public park overlooking the Ohio River in western Louisville on a great expanse of grass and shade trees. There, we join family and friends for the annual community Independence Day celebration and fireworks. It is 1960. I am five years old.

The day offers the sights, sounds, and smells of a big event where it seems everyone knows everyone else. Charcoal smoke rises from park grills where fathers in Bermuda shorts grill hot dogs, bratwursts, and hamburgers while sipping Falls City beers and tossing horseshoes. Mothers in summer dresses push together picnic tables and cover them with tablecloths before they spread out plates of cold fried chicken and ham, bowls of potato salad and baked beans, Jell-O molds, and freshly baked pies. Platters of sliced tomatoes and onions and lettuce are placed beside bottles of ketchup and mustard, ready to dress the burgers as they came off the grill. Watermelons covered with ice lay in metal tubs under the shade of oak trees, waiting to be split open and devoured on this hot summer day. Looking at the bounty of food, I am sure that this will be the best picnic ever.

While waiting for the food to be served, children chase each other, play cards, and start a baseball game at the adjacent ballfield. Nearby, I hear the excited screams of children and teenagers as they speed downhill on the wooden roller coaster at the adjacent Fontaine Ferry Amusement Park, which I later learn is only for white people. Mesmerized, I watch the passengers holding up their arms and waving their hands as the cars slowly climb to the peak of the coaster. Once they reach the top, the passengers' screams and laughter rise above the grinding noise of metal wheels speeding down the tracks.

The scene is so frightening, I have no desire to ever climb into one of the coaster cars and dive down those rickety tracks. Instead, I look to find my adventure on the nearby playground. As I walk toward a group of children on the swings and seesaws, my mother intercepts me. "Come with me," she says sternly. "I do not want you to go anywhere near the playground right now."

I cannot grasp the problem and turn back toward the playground. But my mother yanks my arm and moves me quickly back to the picnic tables. "Listen to me," she commands. "You are not allowed to play with those kind of children."

Those kind of children? What did she mean? I am confused as I look at the children, whose skin is much darker than mine. They are an unfamiliar sight but one that intrigues rather than frightens me.

All the adults in our group stare at the people they see as intruders with disdain.

"Why did they have to come here?" my exasperated mother asks a friend. "They are spoiling everything!"

My father angrily points his Falls City beer bottle at the group before taking a sip of the cold brew. "Damn, I cannot believe they are here," he exclaims to his buddies. "This is *our* park! They have no business being here."

My father begins swinging his arms in the air pointing at the group as he continues. "Yes sir, they are fouling up the park. I can smell them from here." As he rants, his hand stabs his Camel into the air where cigarette smoke accents his ugly words.

I am confused. All I smell is his cigarette mixing in the air with the tantalizing smell of meat ready to come off the grill. I am ready to eat. But for the adults in our group, their appetites are gone. Instead, they focus their attention and white-hot anger at a group of strangers who only want to picnic on a beautiful Fourth of July.

Shawnee Park, like all the other major parks in the city, had been segregated since the parks were established in the early 1900s. But for a few years before our picnic, black people were finally allowed to visit the park. On this Independence Day, a few brave families had gathered in small groups to have their own picnics and fireworks.

But my parents and their friends are in no mood to share the space. For them, the day is ruined. On this Independence Day, their sense of white entitlement is laid bare as they are forced to share this very public space.

This is my first memory of the racism that permeated the segregated world I grew up in. It was a world where the N-word was common, and I was forbidden to associate with black children as long as I lived under my parents' roof. It was a world where the adults continuously resisted the changes created by the civil rights movement.

My parents and their friends refused to hold another Fourth of July picnic at Shawnee Park.

WHAT ARE WE FIGHTING FOR?

Joan Dubay

I heard my name being called long before I saw her. I turned from center field.

"Nancy, phone, waiting, Richard, shot . . ." she gasped.

I threw my baseball mitt on the ground, sprinted across the grassy field and up the hill, tearing up seven flights of stairs to the pay phone's dangling cord at the end of the hall. Terrified eyes pierced through me as two Fitzpatrick Hall residents stood guard. No one was going to hang up the phone until I got there.

"Nancy," I choked out. "What happened?"

She sobbed. I stared out the window next to the elevator, squeezing the black phone receiver. The cloudless blue sky sparkled.

"Protest . . . Cambodia . . . Richard shot . . . wounded . . ." and then the long drone of a disconnect.

That staccato delivery of my friend's words played over and over in my mind.

Protest. Cambodia. Richard shot. Wounded.

I pictured Nancy standing in her Kent State dorm, calling me. A long line of girls waiting with a pocketful of quarters to phone a friend, to phone home, to say, "I wasn't on the Commons. I was not shot. I'm okay."

I pictured Richard . . . shot. By whom? Where? Why? Would he live? I went to my room and turned on my transistor radio to wait for the news on the hour. How could this happen? Protesting was freedom of speech. How could I finish two more weeks of school? *I need to go home now. The hell with finals. I'm moving to Canada.*

We are only 18 or 19 years old, our first year of college nearly complete. "A Bridge Over Troubled Water" oozed out of the speaker. A nausea enveloped me. I scrambled to the bathroom across the hall, yanking open one of the tan institutional metal stall doors. I fell to my knees and barfed. My head felt as if it would split wide open.

Later that night on the evening news, Walter Cronkite told us all what happened that day—May 4, 1970—in Kent, Ohio, at Kent State University. His words punctured my very existence. Student protest. Cambodia. Governor Rhodes. National Guard. Tear gas. Shots. Wounded. Dead. There was silence and standing room only in the lounge as we watched the images of bloodstained pavement, distraught faces of Kent State students, gas-masked faces of National Guardsmen, apologetic politicians, frightened local citizens. I searched those faces, looking for people I knew, my high school friends. Blinded by tears, I saw half of the footage and heard even less.

My mind drifted to the Country Joe and the Fish song from the 1969 Woodstock stage.

We sang it the summer before we set off to college.

> *One, two, three, what are we fightin' for?*
>
> *Don't ask me, I don't give a damn,*
>
> *Next stop is Vietnam.*
>
> *And it's five, six, seven, open up the pearly gates.*
>
> *Well, there ain't no time to wonder why*
>
> *Whoopee we're all gonna die.*

Dying or living should not look like this.

ONE MORE TIME?

Nancy Genevieve, née Steinhauser

"Baby" hardly fits our sagging waistlines   drooping breasts   balding pates.

We stopped being babies
    when our high school high jinks screeched to a halt November 22
sputtered and sobbed through our college years
    when brother Bobby and hero Martin bled before the electronic us
forever lost our innocence
    when our cousin, brother, lover, friend came home wrapped in a flag.

Our finest collective hours came before most of us could legally drink
    our beliefs welded us into a metallic wave so loud
even the generation before us   who had won a world war
    before getting a mortgage, car, mate   sighed
acquiesced at our beliefs in the possible better world.

As the great population born after fathers and mothers
    survived the lost years of their youth
we were suckled hearing lullabies of our strength
    toddled to marches of freedom
believed the patriot rhetoric of justice.

We rekindled hope like morning sun melting away night fog
    stared back without blinking
registered our black brothers and sisters
    marched arm in arm for a human justice run for by Jesse Owens
but denied back home in our country seeped in old ways
    forged in ancient ankle chains   perpetuated in miserly wages.

A caste system of race   gender   ancestry
    lacked the purity of what we had been taught
we rose like the great mushroom cloud
    that both saved lives and mutilated lives
dozed barriers to opportunities that had never been breached before:

    as simple as a Coke at a white soda fountain
    as complex as a child escorted to grade school by four federal marshals

    as simple as women demanding to shoot hoops
    as complex as them working in the coal mines

    as simple as men cradling their children
    as complex as staying home from work to parent

    as simple as flattening curbs for access
    as complex as passing the ADA

as simple as bleeping streetlights
as complex as mainstreamed classrooms

as simple as the knowing
as complex as the doing.

Then   out of such collective force   such idealized changes   such moral imperatives
    we grew rigid   set in our ways   lost our sight along with our vision
dusted off the old barriers   tried to recreate a secure status quo
    alarm systems must-have items   gated neighborhoods premium
prep schools essential.

Children grow hollow-eyed   gaunt in their size-one desperation
    needles of despair litter playgrounds
a vet lives in some corrugated shipping box
    dries his clothes after a rain on the razor wire
which keeps him out of employment.

Did we burn up all our passions   as well as our unborn children's passions
    before the age of thirty? Forty? Sixty?
or   just become too busy to care
    too weary to even cry
too exhausted to lend a shoulder?

Can we breathe our souls back

    braid the million loose ends together   for our collective strength?

At least   One   More   Time?

Or   will we drool on our bed jackets

    having been wheeled to the porch of The Home

wondering where everyone went

    as we blink in the always rising

        morning sun?

An earlier version, "Baby Boomers," appeared in *NYX: Daughter of Chaos*. Eureka, IL: NOX P, 2002. All publication rights held by Nancy Genevieve.

NO RESPECT: A TAIL-END BABY BOOMER'S ELEGY

Joseph Glynn

Remember Johnny?

Host of the *Tonight Show* from 1962 to 1992, Johnny Carson was the undisputed king of late-night television. I had a habit as a teenager of not going off to bed until I saw Carson's opening monologue. The monologue was not just a bunch of stale jokes—instead, it was an insightful, occasionally hilarious wrap-up of the daily news. And Carson had a gift of skewering everyone—including himself and his audience if the previous night's monologue bombed—without hurting people's feelings.

Before comedy clubs, *Saturday Night Live*, and Comedy Central, the *Tonight Show* was the place to see up-and-coming comedians. If a jokester could make Carson and his audience laugh and was invited back multiple times, he or she would virtually be guaranteed to star in a television sitcom, a blockbuster comedy movie, or in the cases of David Letterman, Jay Leno, and Joan Rivers, his or her own late-night talk show.

Whenever Rodney Dangerfield appeared on the *Tonight Show*, it was must-see TV for me. On the surface, Dangerfield was a homely, overweight, middle-aged man who looked more like a frazzled middle school principal or a shady car dealer than a comedian. However, he would bulge his eyes and crack one-liners about his wife, his job, and societal woes quicker than Charles Bronson gunning down criminals in the *Death Wish* movies. At the end of his routines, Dangerfield would sigh, "That's the story of my life . . . I don't get no respect."

Dangerfield's catchphrase can serve as a motto for me and millions of others born from 1960 to 1964. Because we have the misfortune of being born at the tail end of the baby boom, we have had the uncanny knack of getting no respect from our generation.

We don't remember the Happy Days of the 1950s, "I Like Ike," *Howdy Doody*, the original *Mickey Mouse Club*, *Camelot*, the New Frontier, the Great Society, the successful resolution of the Cuban Missile Crisis, the 1963 March on Washington and the inspiring "I Have a Dream Speech," Selma, and civil rights legislation. We were still in diapers or had not been born on the day when John F. Kennedy was assassinated in Dallas. We missed out on the excitement of Beatlemania, the Summer of Love, flower power, and Woodstock.

Instead, we grew up in a time of energy shortages, stagflation, pollution, divorce, drug overdoses, venereal diseases, high taxes, budget deficits, Watergate, ABSCAM, terrorism, the Iranian hostage crisis, Iran-Contra, Disco Duck music, and Disco Demolition Night. From 1968 to 1980 we saw revered figures such as Robert F. Kennedy, Martin Luther King Jr., and John Lennon brutally murdered. We saw George Wallace, Gerald Ford, Ronald Reagan, and Pope John Paul II survive assassination attempts.

While we did not fight in Vietnam, we watched battle footage on the *Huntley-Brinkley Report* and the *Evening News with Walter Cronkite*, listened to antiwar songs on the radio, wore POW bracelets, saw frenzied antiwar demonstrations, and winced in horror when mobs of people tried to climb aboard army helicopters after the fall of Saigon in 1975. In the 1980s, we flocked to theaters to watch Vietnam-themed movies like *Rambo: First Blood Part Two*, *Platoon*, *Good Morning Vietnam*, *Full Metal Jacket*, *The Hanoi Hilton*, and *Born on the Fourth of July*.

Tail-end boomers were told any child can grow up and become an astronaut. We were elated when Neil Armstrong landed on the moon in 1969 and said, "One small step for man. One giant leap for mankind." The next year, the Apollo 13 spaceflight captivated us more than *Sesame Street*, *Captain Kangaroo*, and Saturday morning cartoons. However, the moon landings soon ended, Skylab fell out space, and except for *Star Wars* and *Star Trek* movies and an occasional science fiction series like *Battlestar Galactica* and *Space 1999*, interest in space had waned by the end of the 1970s. In 1986, we saw the dark side of space exploration when the space craft *Challenger* exploded. We mourned over the loss of elder baby boomer Christa McAuliffe because she looked and acted like the schoolteacher who could conquer the Final Frontier with her intelligence, effervescent personality, and winning smile.

Despite witnessing all these events, tail-end boomers weren't regarded as rebels with and without causes. Instead, we bedeviled our teachers and parents with our sloppy dress, unkempt long hair, surly attitudes, and street smarts. We had the lowest SAT scores on record; the report *A Nation at Risk* stated that if a foreign nation had imposed the mediocre performance of our schools it would be perceived as an act of war. Television shows like *Welcome Back, Kotter* portrayed us as wisecracking clods engaging in Three Stooges-like pratfalls. But at least we knew about how a bill passed through Congress and the functions of conjunctions, thanks to *Schoolhouse Rock.*

Since "sex, drugs, and rock and roll" was one of our mantras, a crackdown was probably inevitable. Herpes and AIDS put a crimp in our sex lives; church-based groups formed to protest the "evil influences" in our music, especially heavy metal. Nancy Reagan launched her "Just Say No" campaign against drugs, and the legal drinking age was raised to 21 in every state. Once in a rare while, tail-end boomers fought back, despite being labeled by elder boomer activists as "apathetic." The most violent riot I ever saw occurred at Illinois State University in 1984 when mobs of angry students rebelled against drinking laws.

The notion of affordable higher education for all was becoming as anachronistic as panty raids and goldfish-eating contests by the time we headed off to college. Tuitions began to skyrocket, federal funding for higher education and Pell Grants were cut. We were the first people to deal with the problem of student debt. Once again, the education we received came under attack. Right-wing critics of academia denounced our Marxist professors as well as the majors that were created in the aftermath of 1960s' demonstrations such as black studies, women's studies, Chicano studies, environmental studies, and peace studies. E. D. Hirsch Jr.'s *Cultural Literacy* criticized us for not knowing certain facts that an "educated" person should know, while Allan Bloom's *The Closing of the American Mind* castigated the "moral relativism" on campuses.

Unlike our elder boomer siblings, we tail-end boomers didn't have the luxury of studying anything we wanted because we knew we had a lucrative middle-class life waiting for us if we just took a bath, had a positive mental attitude, put on a fancy suit, and got a job in plastics. If we committed the cardinal sin of majoring in history, philosophy, anthropology, archaeology, English literature, music, or drama, we faced the prospect of driving taxis, delivering pizzas, or working as janitors for the rest of our lives unless we went off to law school, or we were extremely fortunate to find a tenured professorship at Directional State College—Tank Town Campus. Yet, we were criticized for being too materialistic and too career-oriented. Majoring in business or computer science seemed to be our only shot at the American Dream.

Our progress up the corporate ladder was stymied because of all the older boomers ahead of us. Millions of us were downsized and outsourced, thanks to free trade treaties, the success of books like *Reengineering the Corporation*, corporate raiders such as Carl Icahn and junk bond king Michael Milken, and the lean-and-mean attitude that turned "Neutron" Jack Welch and "Chainsaw" Al Dunlap into celebrities, rather than obscure CEOs. Then, there was the 1987 stock market collapse, the 2000 dot-com collapse, the Enron fiasco, and the greed-is-good mentality that engulfed Wall Street and corporate America.

Then came the Great Recession of 2008.

This economic calamity hit tail-end boomers especially hard. We faced the predicament of being too young to collect Social Security checks and too old to reinvent ourselves in a lucrative new career. Many of us were 99-ers (people who had been out of work for 99 weeks or more) or never found another job again. Others fell victim to the opioids epidemic that swept the country during the second decade of the 21st century. And still others were working in the type of menial jobs in retail and restaurants we held as high school and college students, or we held no-benefit, no-security, "gig economy" positions like Uber drivers.

Not surprisingly, our upcoming "golden years" don't look too golden. In the *Harvard Business Review*, New School economist Teresa Ghilarducci and Blackstone executive vice chairman Tony James have argued that the United States will be seeing elder poverty not experienced since the Great Depression. Maybe to survive in our retirement years, many of us are going to grit our teeth, roll our eyes, hold our noses, and marry millionaires like the elderly lecherous playboy Osgood Fielding III from the movie *Some Like it Hot*. After all, nobody's perfect.

Certainly, being born in the final years of the baby boom has been anything but idyllic. Tail-end boomers have learned that life is not like a perpetual Disneyland. We seem destined to be like Leo Durocher's proverbial nice guys—no matter how hard we try, we always seem to finish last, plus we don't get any credit for our efforts.

Yet, I have found the lack of respect does have its upsides.

For one thing, it has not made me blithely sanguine. My wife, who was born near the beginning of the baby boom and tries to keep a positive view of life, often calls me "a cynical pessimist." But I don't consider myself a cynical pessimist as much as a realist. I know most of us tail-end boomers will agree with the late comedian George Carlin, the American Dream is just a dream "because you have to be asleep to believe it." I also know too many "respectable" people in the highest echelons of society lie, cheat, steal, and do anything but walk the straight and narrow.

The older I get, the more I agree with the adage that respect is something that must be earned, not given out on a silver platter. For instance, when I left the world of academe an eon or two ago to find a job in the "real world," I thought employers would be so overjoyed over my grade point average and my credentials that I would have a gold key to the executive suite in no time. Little did I know that my fancy degrees, my glowering letters of recommendation, and my well-crafted résumé meant nothing because I had no practical experience. It took a long time before anyone would hire me.

Getting no respect sometimes has given me a great sense of humor. If laughter is truly the best medicine, then I need it like the flimflammed pioneers at Wild West vaudeville shows demanding cases of snake oil. I can look at the mistakes made by the movers and shakers in society and chuckle, "Boy, are they dumb schmucks." But I can laugh at my own innumerable foibles, throughout my life, as well.

EVERYTHING TILTS

Kari Gunter-Seymour

"You measure a democracy by the freedom it gives its dissidents."
—Abbie Hoffman

A clutch of adjectives
and the term *disillusioned* to speak of us.
Paisleyed and flower-painted,
our frankness spread by mouths
and underground presses.

Ho, ho. Hey, hey.
How many babies have you killed today?

Stern winds. Night walked freely the ranks
of the sun, choked under a pillow of clouds.
Four bodies, shadows long,
streets smeared and lost.

What became of us once we'd been
torn apart and returned to our future,
reduced to radical clearness?
How fragile the axis upon which
everything tilts, left to its own dank devices.

CLUELESS

Suzanne Hartman

My brother-in-law is a 60-year old black man. He is a fine person who I love and welcome to my home with open arms. Yet, when we invited him to stay there with my sister one weekend while we were away, he hesitated, worried the neighbors would wonder why a black man was there. He was afraid he would be mistaken for an intruder. At the time, I felt his concern was over the top. Now I know I was clueless.

As a white woman, I take it for granted that my life has unfolded on a relatively level playing field. I use the word *relatively* because being female meant limited options until the women's movement raised our collective consciousness and ushered in the start of a new era. However, I never questioned my freedom to go where I chose.

Louisville, 1946. The year of my birth. A predictable white, middle-class world. My dad worked and my mom was a homemaker. Rosie the Riveter was expected to turn in her tools and vacate her place on the line to returning GIs. Kids played outdoors and went to neighborhood schools. I lived in a small house my father bought with his GI benefits, at a time when black GIs were denied equal access to jobs in the post-war boom. Redlining prevented them from buying homes in many neighborhoods. Their children attended segregated schools. The insidious cruelty of the Jim Crow era continued, but I knew none of this.

I never actually knew a black person during my childhood. I saw black laborers on construction sites when I accompanied my father in the summer to deliver payroll. I was in the third grade when segregated schools were ruled unconstitutional. My world remained unchanged. I attended a private, Catholic school. There were no black families on our street.

I was acquainted with only one black person. Her name was Emma and she came to our house by bus every two weeks to iron our clothes, standing for long hours on the basement concrete floor, smoothing the wrinkles in starched shirts, sheets, pillowcases, cotton dresses. I looked forward to those afternoons, talking with her as I sat on the basement step and ate my after-school snack. She was a "domestic" then.

I remember the first time I heard my beloved grandmother use the N-word. I was only about 10 years old; its ugliness startled me. Something about it conflicted with my view of my grandmother as a loving and generous woman. She was born just 30 years after the Civil War. I suppose she had been conditioned to think that way growing up in the South.

It was not until I started working in the business world that I began to take slow steps towards discerning the nature of inequality based on race. Affirmative action programs began to affect personnel selection. I was an experienced service representative with the telephone company, charged with training the first black employee in our department. I can still hear my supervisor telling me, "Make her a service representative," a position that did not fit her skill set. I argued with her that there were positions in the company she could succeed in, but I was told that was not an option. It occurred to me then that they wanted her for her skin color. Eventually she quit. Like me, this was her first job after she graduated from high school. Sometimes I wonder what she did next.

I began my career in teaching in a Louisville inner-city school in the '70s. It was 1971 and I was selected to be in the vanguard of desegregation as public schools integrated their teaching staff. It had been many years since the *Brown vs. Board of Education* ruling in 1954. I was one of three new white faculty members. My family and friends automatically feared for my safety. I did not share their concern. I was simply eager to test my new skills. I was surprised by the cool reception I received from my colleagues. Now I understand why. I imagine they were suspicious about my ability to meet the needs of black students. I was the first white person some of the second graders in my classroom had met. When we went on a field trip to the zoo, it was, for some, the first venture outside of their immediate neighborhood.

After I divorced, I had to rebuild my life. I was able to find a job and safe, affordable housing for my children. In 1990, I returned to school to earn a graduate degree in psychology. As a therapist, I am frequently confronted with issues of race and diversity. Recently, I met with a patient who expressed concern for the welfare of her biracial, teenage son who, at 14, is typically outspoken and resentful of authority. Her worry is compounded by her fear that he will "go off" on a police officer. What then? Will he be given a fair chance at justice? Will anyone try to understand his behavior from a developmental perspective rather than a racial one? She had discussed her fears with her son. This is not the same conversation white mothers have with their teenagers.

To this day, my brother-in-law is cautious in his public behavior. I remember a recent evening at the movies with him and my sister. We had gone to see *Fences*. After the movie, my sister and I made a beeline for the restroom, asking our husbands to hold our coats and purses. My brother-in-law refused and said, "No, no, someone might think I stole it."

Louisville made national headlines in 2016. Homicides reached 112, highest in five decades. Police blamed drugs, gangs, and guns in the hands of impulsive teens and young adults as key factors. About 60 percent of the victims were black. They lived in areas with high poverty and bleak job prospects. Two black people were killed here in a Kroger grocery store in a racially motivated shooting.

Black Lives Matter was created in 2012 after 17-year-old Trayvon Martin's killer was acquitted. It is a call to action and a response to the racism that continues to permeate our society. Many white citizens dismiss it. "All lives matter" is their rallying cry. I believe the organization is needed. How long will it take for white citizens to at least acknowledge the disparity their "privilege" has caused for black individuals?

There has been progress in the movement for civil rights in my lifetime. However, there is still much to do to extend full and equal rights to all citizens. Many white Americans look at black, inner-city communities and count them out, ignoring the danger of radical indifference. Social and economic isolation produces a volatile subculture left out of mainstream America. Some black youth are written off as "thugs."

The struggle for basic rights that are naturally my birthright continues.

I find this reality offensive. I am aware that I am privileged in ways my black brothers and sisters are not, though try as I will I can never fully grasp the burden and pain that overshadows their lives. I will remain clueless.

My brother-in-law did finally agree to stay in our home while we were away; he agreed to it only after I contacted the police officer who patrolled our modest neighborhood, explaining his presence, describing the strange car that would be parked in the driveway. Now I know that his fear is righteous, the legacy of racism's history of discrimination and unspeakable cruelty. How very sad that he still has to scale this barrier.

THE WHOLE WORLD IS WATCHING

Lennie Hay

valentine's day footprints, tracks of blood.
       Hands on shoulders. Heads down.
Lines of armed police create a path
       from dead classmates, bloodied teacher.
They search for pathway as the young did

watching 50 years ago. Promises broken by middle-aged
       white men dropping bombs, drafting the young.
Protestors marched Michigan Avenue, crowded Grant Park.
       Frozen black-and-white photos showed
collisions, mace and billy club eruptions

watching August swastikas, torches burn holes
       in Charlottesville's streets young men,
tight knots of rage. Clashes. Crashes. Blood curses
       contaminate streets, mow down a young
believer. *There can be no blame on both sides for murder*

watching a voice silenced in Memphis. Another felled,

    a graceful Sequoia stretched future-bound in LA.

Words, miserable retorts. A country stands

    guilty on broken bodies, stained young souls

strain to accept the sins of their elders

watching Chicago's words held high—*Dow earns while people burn.*

    watch Florida's young chant a choice—*Children or guns.*

A tunnel strewn with condolences and corpses

    yet we eat our young.

Sin simmers

    50 years

vultures overhead

    snatch breadcrumbs.

CHILD OF THE SIXTIES

John Limeberry

I don't remember John Kennedy's assassination. I was born in 1962, the beginning of the end of the baby boom generation. I once heard it said that if one does not remember the fall of Camelot or the rise of the Fab Four, he/ she is not really in the club, the great demographic phenomenon—a batch of babies born to horny heroes who had saved the world from Hitler. A massive collection of comrades who, by the sheer weight of their numbers, would crush 1950s' sensibilities of decorum and conformity, and dare to change the world. Of course, many of them went into real estate development and voted for Reagan, but let's not tarnish the myth or scar the ones who held onto their ideals with the sins of those who have gone astray. Let's get back to me.

State Road 56 runs between Paoli and Salem in southern Indiana. There's not much that distinguishes it from a dozen other Indiana highways. If you drive it, you'll pass cows and cornfields. You'll see barns bearing the date they were constructed, and the ubiquitous basketball goal. If you happen to pass close enough when a farmer is tending the field from inside a tractor cabin, you will always get a wave. Hoosier hospitality is not a lie.

A few miles and a couple of rolling hills outside Paoli lies Stamper's Creek cemetery. Both my parents reside there now, but my father has been there since 1964. I never knew him. I know he was successful at business. He owned and operated a skid factory, producing wooden pallets that were used in material handling and logistics applications. He was already 50 when I was born, somewhat old now—certainly old then. I'm told he was a good man. I hope he was. However, he seems to have been a typical man of his generation. He worked hard, he provided for his family, and he drank. I lost him to cirrhosis when I was two. I don't mean him any disrespect. I have no anger toward him, just regret that I have nothing to base any feelings on at all. As such, the conclusion I'm left with is that he was a good man who lost the battle with the bottle.

I was a child of a single mom when single moms were not commonplace. It was kind of like an early version of *The Gilmore Girls*, except for the gender, the geographic location, and the perfectly peppered popular culture references. I was born at the twilight of the baby boom generation. One could argue that I am not the most obvious representative of a culture-shocking generation. However, there must be some nostalgic value in remembering what it was like to be a *child* in the '60s.

Perhaps the best description I can give is that I lived through an elementary *Wonder Years*. My mother transplanted form Paoli to Salem, Indiana, after my father's death, and in 1968, I entered the halls of Bradie M. Shrum Elementary School. No, it hadn't been renamed after Robert F. Kennedy, as had Kevin Arnold's junior high.

Salem wasn't really big enough to have suburbs, but I did live in a nice section of town called Fair Acres, so named because of its proximity to the Washington County Fair Grounds. So, every July, in the sweltering heat and humidity of a typical Indiana summer, we were only a short walk from carousels and cotton candy. You could sit in the backyard and hear the echoes from the demolition derby, or the amplified sounds of whatever musical act had found its way into the bleacher-filled entertainment venue.

Our home was, more or less, like all of the other tranquil domiciles in the neighborhood, a one-story red brick with attached carport. There were few actual garages in the neighborhood, but carports were plentiful. Ours was home to a white Ford Galaxy 500. I don't know in what year it was manufactured, but it lasted into the '70s. I don't remember seat belts. I know there was no air conditioner. Instead, you could open vents on the underside of the dash, which allowed outside air to rush into the automobile. The cooling effect may have been more of an illusion, but we were content. Another win for the "ignorance is bliss" crowd.

The home did have an air conditioner. One air conditioner, in a window, and in a corner bedroom. The cooling effect worked, but, of course, it was not even-handed. In order for the living room to be comfortable, the bedroom with the device had to be freezing.

I must admit we did live in the living room. And in the middle of that room was the greatest device of all, the television. It basically raised me. There weren't that many channels from which to choose, and as I will explain, my choices were even more limited. Still, the television set had become ubiquitous by the mid-1960s. Ours was the centerpiece of the living room. A 1957 RCA Victor, it sat inside its own stand-alone cabinet. Two cabinet doors could open up to reveal the screen and close again when the TV was not in use.

Two channels may seem ridiculous by today's standards. Our set only received a VHF signal. Salem received its television signals from the three broadcast stations located in Louisville. The NBC and CBS affiliates had a VHF signal, but the ABC affiliate was UHF. I would not consistently see ABC programming until well into the 1970s. This means that, even today, I will miss references to *The Brady Bunch*.

This was before MTV, with its 24-hour-a-day smorgasbord of music videos . . . okay, not the best reference. There was no Cartoon Network, with its 24-hour-a-day smorgasbord of kid-oriented clips . . . there that's better. But I think we had something just as good, made better by the fact that we had to wait for gratification. We couldn't just randomly tune in and find a show like *Robot Chicken*. No, we had to bide our time for Saturday mornings. For a real child of the '60s, it didn't get much better than Saturday morning cartoons. I knew the schedule by heart.

I would get up early, sit much too close to the television set, and turn the volume down low so as not to wake my sleeping mother. I was a terribly spoiled child, but one of the few things that could result in my mother's wrath was waking her up from a good night's sleep. I might not only lose television privileges for the rest of the day, but she might just break out the fly swatter she used for corporeal punishment. Go ahead and laugh, but on a bare arm or leg the damn thing stung.

Some favorite Saturday offerings were the anthropomorphic *Banana Splits* and the eponymous *H. R. Pufnstuf*, where Puf worked to save Jimmy (and his talking flute friend Freddy) from the snatches of the wicked Witchiepoo. However, the highlight of Saturday morning had to be *The Herculoids*. We were told by the impressive, booming voice-over that they lived somewhere out in space. Granted, that didn't really narrow it down much, but we understood. The lead Hercules-like character was Zandor. Tara was his seductively drawn, leggy wife. At the time, I wasn't sure why I liked Tara, but there was something about her. Dorno was their son. Hercules and Tara fought off evil space pirates with Dorno and their dependable, other-worldly, animal friends, which included a flying space dragon, a giant rock-ape, a four-horned triceratops character, and last but not least, Gloop and Gleep, two protoplasmic characters who could form themselves into shields or trampolines or almost anything else

I had a superhero affliction, and every weekday afternoon at four, *Batman* aired on the local ABC station. Now, I was not even a reader of Batman comics because, early on, I was drawn to the Marvel Universe much more so than the worlds of DC. For the most part, I was content with two channels until one Florida vacation, when I chose to stay in the hotel room and watch television rather than go to the ocean. I perused the television guide and spied a 3:00 p.m. showing of *The Avengers*. I was in a state of eight-year-old surprise and giddiness because I knew that no show featuring Iron Man and Thor was being telecast into southern Indiana. All those expectations, of course, came crashing down when I tuned in at three and saw some detective drama with bowler hats and English accents. I saw Emma Peele. I wouldn't see the ocean for 12 years.

Still, a superhero is a superhero, and *Batman* was must-see TV. Fortunately, neighbors knew neighbors in 1960-era Salem, and neighborhood kids knew neighborhood kids, and the neighbors had TVs that got UHF, and thus, ABC, and therefore, *Batman*. The only decision was whose house would be hosting on any given day. The Baker boys lived across the street. Stew was a year older than me, and Lenny was a year younger. The Boyd girls, Grace and Donna, lived next door. I asked Donna to marry me once; I think she said, "yes." But the best place to go was up the street, to the hill, where the Robinson house was located. Ronnie and his older sister, Meredith, lived there. There was a television in the corner of the finished basement, which also had a bar and bar stools. It all seemed very modern and chic. And to top it all off, they had a *color* television. Adam West never looked so good.

One afternoon while watching the caped crusader at the Boyd house, the brakes of a passing car failed, sending the auto through a stop sign and into an embankment. Word is it was a fairly loud crash. I never heard it. The lure of the ambulance, whose attendants helped the shaken driver from the car, forced everyone out into the yard to watch. I dutifully tagged along, but I was secretly hoping we were only going to spend a commercial break outside.

Of course, emergency vehicles and dump trucks did fascinate us. We rode our banana-seat Schwinns with playing cards stuck in the spokes to add a whipping sound effect to the rotating tires, while mimicking as best we could the siren call of firetrucks or police cruisers.

Remember your first bike? What am I saying? Of course you do. July 1, 1968, my sixth birthday: I remember my mother leading me to the utility closet, opening the door, and stepping aside so that I could see the red, two-wheeled present that waited inside. As my friends and I grew more confident, we took more and more chances. Inspired by the daredevil riders who would perform annually at the county fair, we placed boards over bricks to be utilized as launching pads for our exploits.

There was a hill that separated the Boyd girls' house from mine. We practiced "crashing" bikes by descending the hill, picking up speed, and then jumping from the bike just before the grass gave way to the Boyds' concrete driveway. When I go back now, I'm struck by how small the hill is, but to a six-year old, it possessed the danger of a Thunderdome.

You could be a daredevil on Saturday afternoon, but you still found yourself in church on Sunday morning. My mother and I drifted through several denominations. Too young to adequately discern the slight differences in doctrine, I found them to be mostly the same. I have no artistic ability whatsoever, so my attempts at coloring Jonah in the whale or Moses holding the Ten Commandments were never worthy of refrigerator magnets, but I got a good grounding in the stories of the Bible from elderly Sunday School teachers whose patience and devotion were truly heaven sent.

I can't say I enjoyed the sermons. Whether bombastic or sublime, they always lasted too long. However, I found that if I rested my elbows on my knees, and knelt my head forward, putting me in sort of a praying pose, I could make hand shadow puppets on the wooden floor below the pew.

I often enjoyed the music. It would be a few more years before '60s' sensibilities and rock chords would make their way into the Christian music canon, but I knew a few hymns. I would sing those hymns, too, even if the congregation was singing something else. I was nothing if not a trendsetter, and I would not be silenced.

My mother and I paraded across the Protestant spectrum, Baptist Church to Christian Church to Methodist Church. We even stopped in with the Nazarenes for a spell, but they were a bit too restrictive. They don't even go to movies.

We went to movies. No, there was no air-conditioned cinema with Sensurround technology, but there was the Salem Drive-In. Here again, I may be separated from my older brethren within the boomer community. While they may have used the facility as a darkened corner for carnal delights, being six or seven, I came for the show, and the intermission jingle of "Let's all go to the lobby" because that meant hot dogs and Cokes.

I saw the animated version of *The Jungle Book* there. Being sucked in by Disney's well-executed television commercial campaign, I looked forward to that show with the anticipation of Christmas, a snow day, and summer vacation all rolled into one. Even though I was disappointed when Mowgli decided to leave his friends for the company of a girl, it was still an exhilarating experience.

Also, being a pint-sized paleontologist wannabe, I saw *The Valley of Gwangi*. Don't remember it? Don't worry. But, just to satisfy everyone's curiosity, Gwangi was an angry allosaurus. The film contained violent special effects for the time, but I got through it. I couldn't say that for a couple of the vampire films, which had me lying down in the back seat with my eyes closed—now I had something in common with those older boomers who were parked a few rows back.

No nostalgic walk through the Hoosier hinterlands of the 1960s would be complete without an examination of pastimes and pastry, card games and cuisine. All right, enough alliteration, I'm talking about euchre and persimmon pudding. I could be corrected, but I'm of the opinion that nowhere outside of southern Indiana would a child grow up with the touchstones of the card game, euchre, and the dessert, persimmon pudding. The former being a complicated challenge, best learned young. It's much easier to grow up playing euchre than to try to master the alternating power of jacks, called bowers, depending on the current trump situation, etc., etc., as an adult. In much the same way, Hoosier youth acquire a taste for the tart persimmon pudding dessert, created by using the pulp of the indigenous fruit. Those not accustomed to the taste who encounter it later in life, usually by a pushy promoter who promises them that they will love it, may give a polite, "it's okay" or the less promising, "it's different," but they will never reach the heights of culinary rapture felt by those raised on the stuff. I mean, have you ever tasted Vegemite?

So, in the final analysis, from my perspective, that of a true child of the '60s growing up in the Ohio Valley, life passed quietly and happily, and most importantly, peacefully. My friends and I were shielded in our small-town cocoon from the political earthquakes and violent circumstances endured by older baby boomers. Life was birthday parties, county fairs, and visits from a small traveling circus. It was football, baseball, and especially basketball (it was Indiana, for God' sake) in summer. New math and flutophone bands during the school year. And, oh, to be the only child of a single mother with resources at Christmas.

Every year, I would crazily circle desired items in the Sears Christmas Catalog/Wish Book. And every year, while I slept, those items, wrapped in packages of red, gold, and green would accumulate under our silver Christmas tree. The tree turned different colors, thanks to a fancy little contraption that consisted of a light with a spinning wheel in front of it made of different colors of glass. When the red portion of the wheel passed in front of the light, the tree would take on a reddish hue, blue when the blue portion of the wheel was illuminated, and so forth.

I would always promise my mother on Christmas Eve, that no matter how many gifts surrounded the tree on Christmas morning, I would eat breakfast before opening any of them. Never trust the promises of a six-year-old. I would eagerly tear into the holiday treasures, everything from Hot Wheel sets to Rock 'Em Sock 'Em Robots.

Of course, the omnipresent television still held a place of importance. Holiday cartoons were must-see TV. *How the Grinch Stole Christmas* was probably my favorite. I'd watch *Rudolph, the Red-Nosed Reindeer*, even though the Abominable Snow Monster of the North scared the hell out of me. And, of course, there was *A Charlie Brown Christmas*. Every year, I got to hear the reading from Luke, a rendition of "Hark the Herald Angels Sing," and be sucked in by those commercials for Zingers. And, in the end, it wasn't such a bad little tree.

So, as the world raged around us, children maintained their innocence. John Kennedy was taken from us while I was learning to walk. The Beatles exploded into living rooms across the country while I was learning to talk. Martin Luther King Jr. was assassinated, and I watched *Bonanza*. Robert Kennedy was shot in California, and I was safely asleep, three time zones away. Vietnam protestors were beaten in the streets of Chicago, while I was surviving skinned knees from jumping out of swings.

It would be almost a decade before I would listen to artifacts of the age with any clarity—"Eve of Destruction" or *Sgt. Pepper's Lonely Hearts Club Band*. I had more Monkees' albums than Beatles.

In the final analysis, I think it's true. If one doesn't remember JFK's assassination or the Beatles on *The Ed Sullivan Show*, he/she can't really understand the boomer experience. We're like younger brothers and sisters watching an older sibling drive away in his or her first car. We can hop in our plastic Big Wheel but can go to the edge of the driveway.

Still, we don't choose our time in this world; we can only make the best of the time we have. Fate placed me at the beginning of the end of one of the most influential generations in American history, and I don't take that lightly.

Perhaps, the actual children of the '60s are the most fortunate of all. We're close enough in time to adhere to the ideals of the envelope pushers without suffering any of the paper cuts. Maybe that sounds selfish. Maybe it is.

Sue me; I'm an only child (of the '60s). Peace.

LONG TIME COMING

Don Krieger

The house fires were always in colored town.
Dad called them less fortunate. We were cold
and hungry too, but different; we were meant
for college.

The missile crisis came. Castro had nukes.
Bombers flew over every few minutes.
Convoys ran Dixie Highway for weeks
so it was hard crossing to school.

We had no basement for shelter. I dug a hole
in the yard one time. It filled with sea water.
We were drilled in class, marched to the closet
to cower. When Nixon got in,

I was terrified,
thought he might use nukes in Vietnam,
burn everything clean.

A WOMAN'S WORLD

Colleen McCormick

I was eight years old the first time I attended a protest. Actually, I was eight years old the first time I *remembered* attending a protest. My mother had informed my father we needed to head out to the grocery for a few supplies she desperately needed for the dinner casserole.

"Didn't you go to the grocery yesterday?" he had asked her, as she collected our coats from the hall closet.

"You know me," my mother said. She laughed. "I can't even remember everything I've written on the list! I forgot the breadcrumbs yesterday."

"Avoid downtown," he had warned her as she tugged at the zipper on my winter coat, strapping me into the navy-blue marshmallow suit. "It's going to be a zoo today." He sipped his cream-no-sugar coffee from the chipped white mug he always used and walked into his den.

The November air was rough against my cheeks as my mother held my hand tightly and tugged me toward the bus stop at the end of our street. That day, we didn't go to the grocery. We went somewhere else. It was a place of wonder and awe as throngs of people crowded together, chanting words that brought tears to their eyes. Women, hand in hand, shouted and cheered words I could not comprehend. My mother pulled me alongside her, my little legs struggling to keep up with the stride of the crowd.

It was the first time I vividly remember my mother being happy. There was a glimmer in her eye as she roared with the crowd, her fist in the air. She was beautiful, carefree.

On the ride back, my mother held me closely. My fingers were numb, and my cheeks were flushed.

"One day, women will be able to choose if they want babies or careers or both. That belief is what brought us women together today, baby."

I nuzzled into her warmth and inhaled her comforting smell of vanilla and musk.

"When you're older, I'll tell you all about Margaret Sanger, okay? But for now, today will be our little secret, right, Joan?" she murmured. The bus jostled back and forth, and I drifted off to sleep.

"It's going to be a woman's world," was my mother's most memorable line. As she vacuumed the formal living room for one of our annual dinner parties, when she pulled a pie out of the oven with the crust slightly darker than the golden brown the recipe suggested, as she ironed my school skirt on Sunday nights frustrated that it was never as smooth as the skirt my friend Marie wore, she'd say to herself, "It's going to be a woman's world."

Yet, there was a fire that raged behind those wide brown eyes, a spark that had been ignited long ago and never dulled, the one that deemed her different. My father, on the other hand, with his crystal blue eyes and light hair, looked the part of a true American boy. The stern and brash expression that never faltered was a product of the years he spent in the army and the atrocities he had seen, the ones of which he never spoke, but we had learned about in European history my freshman year of high school.

The two were an unlikely pair. I had never believed in the fairytale type of love that most of my friends and classmates had throughout their childhoods. My parents had a different type of love. I had never known why. As a child, I thought it normal for the pies to be burnt. I assumed the wrinkles in his shirts, despite having been pressed, were a demonstration of character, not a silent act of defiance. I never paid mind to the chaotic and crooked lines from the vacuum, or the underlying tale of resentment they told. I assumed everyone's parents had fallen into a comfortable silence with few gestures of intimacy and rare conversation, usually pertaining to the weather or the dinner menu.

I had always wondered how they had come together.

At age 13, I learned that my mother did not want to be a mother. I had snuck into my parents' room one Saturday evening when they had gone to the McGregors' for dinner and drinks, a party deemed unfit for any of the children. I had always wondered what the box underneath my parents' bed contained. Ever since I was young, after my father had commented on the charred dinner dish or the haphazard vacuum lines, I would find my mother upstairs, her knees tucked to her chest, the box in front of her resting on the afghan my grandmother had knitted for my parents on their wedding day.

When I came into the room, she would shut the box, wipe the tears from her brown eyes, smile, and say, "Joan, I thought you were downstairs with your father."

The thought of the secrets in Mom's small oak chest was enough to make my palms sweat. The door to my parents' room creaked when I pushed it open. It was eerily silent in the house; the only sound was the beating of my own heart inside my ears as I crouched down and pulled the box from underneath the bed. The box was simple, plain. It was a dark honey color, smooth to the touch. There was a single chip on one of the edges. It was lighter than I expected as I unlatched the golden lock and opened what felt like the only treasure chest I had ever found.

I learned a lot of things the day I opened that box. My parents had met at a diner in 1939. My mother had gone to the restaurant with her friends; my father had done the same. He introduced himself to her on a dare from his friends, and the rest was history. Their love had swept my mother off her feet. She swooned for my father's cerulean eyes and hearty laugh, or so I had read in the correspondence between my mother and her older sister.

My mother had, at the time, fallen madly in love with my father.

"He always makes me laugh," she wrote to my Aunt Nancy, "and he always makes me feel valued."

She tried to be the woman that she thought he wanted. More importantly, she tried to be the woman she thought he needed. She wanted to be a good housewife and even more, a good mother to all six children they talked about having one day.

But then the war came. And my father was drafted and served overseas. It was a difficult time for my mother, who had already birthed my older brother, Matthew. My father went to fight the Nazis, and my mother went to work on a factory line. Suddenly a single mother and a working woman, my mother felt abandoned and helpless. She helped make ammunition for the guns that people like my father were holding to defend freedom all over the world.

"It is nice to know that maybe, just maybe, Jim is being protected by the work I am trying to do here," she wrote to her sister. "It makes me feel a little less sick with worry. I hope they return soon."

But, as I continued to read, the letters revealed her transformation. "I find meaning in the work I am doing. I love getting my hands dirty. I feel useful after a long day on the line."

Her letters became less and less about the work she continued to do as the men fought tirelessly for our lives. Instead, they divulged a difficult realization for my mother. "I hear there is an end in sight, and it scares me. I don't want to go back to who I was, Nancy. I was trapped. Confined. Caged. I have found a new meaning, a new understanding, a type of freedom I had never dreamed possible. I thought motherhood would bring that freedom, Nancy. It never did. I worry Jim will never understand."

Her words become more distraught as I continued to read on.

"I'm tired, Nancy. Tired of the screaming and the teething and waking up in the middle of the night to feed him. Is this normal? I don't think I was cut out to be a mother." And in the last letter, written on only a single scrap of paper, were a few lines that are burned forever in my memory: "It's been six months since I've last written you. Jim is home. Things are different. I can't explain how, but I feel it in the depths of my being. I'm three weeks late to my period and I can't breathe."

The words echo in my mind: *I'm three weeks late to my period and I can't breathe.* I heard them as I carefully placed each letter back in its rightful spot and tucked the box underneath the bed. They whispered softly as I ran the bath and sat quietly in the lukewarm water, my knees tucked to my chest. They wrapped themselves around me as I crawled into bed and tried not to cry.

The realization and understanding of how much it physically hurt my mother when I came along set in.

The first time I asked my mother about the letters, I thought she would be angry that I had taken it upon myself to open the only key to her buried past. Instead, she smiled softly as she stood over the pan on the stovetop; the bacon crackling was the only sound for a long while.

"I always wondered when you were going to take it upon yourself to find out what was in that box." She took a deep breath. "I want you to know, Joan, I have always and will always love you."

She did not turn to look at me, but I saw her shoulders tense. We both felt the heavy cloud of what was not spoken: the words from the last letter, the words that were always a whisper in the back of my mind.

"You are one of the biggest blessings of my life. Don't ever forget that."

She did not apologize. I know she was not sorry for the words she wrote, her own truth of sorts. But I took her words then for what they were.

"I always wanted a little girl," she said quietly.

"What was it like working in the factory?" I asked before the tears I felt in the corner of my eyes had the chance to fall. I heard my father at the top of the stairs. He coughed and descended the staircase, into the foyer. There was the same glimmer in her eye I had seen at the protest. No anger, no hurt. There was only a distant expression, a longing for a different time.

"It was magical, Joan, absolutely magical," she said as my father entered the kitchen.

————

On my 14th birthday, my mother told me about the conversation she and my father had had after he returned from the war. She wanted so desperately to continue to work. As the letters had revealed, she found meaning in the grueling work that she genuinely enjoyed, found worth in receiving her biweekly pay. My father, apparently, had scoffed and waved her off. After all, it was a man's job to earn the money and what would that say of my father, of my family, if my mother continued to seek employment after the war?

That year, my mother had given me a family heirloom. A pearl necklace her mother had received on her wedding day, passed down to my mother on the day she wed my father.

"It's beautiful," I said.

"I want to give it to you now so you know you can do and be more than a wife," my mother said. She wrapped the string of pearls around my neck. I felt the weight of the expectation she had for me to defy the system as she clasped it.

"It's going to be a woman's world one day, Joan," my mother had said. "Chaos is brewing. Things are changing." Her eyes were distant, somewhere else. She took a step back and smoothed her apron down. "Just you wait."

I remember the way my mother hovered at the arm of the couch as my father listened to the evening news. There were protests and marches lead by Martin Luther King Jr. Sit-ins and teach-ins held by the students. My mother perched, her hands clasped tightly in her lap, her ears attuned to the static reception of the television as my father flipped through the newspaper, a cigar in his left hand, and a scotch, neat, on the table in front of him. I sat at the desk, pretended to fiddle with my homework problems; my parents were unaware of how much I had begun to understand.

I began to understand the chaos. The hippies wanted love and black people wanted justice, and women wanted a new understanding, while my mother fought with my father for me to go to college. He refused. Explained it was a waste of time when there was a perfectly fine secretarial position available in my Uncle Ted's office building.

"Times are changing!" she had screamed at my father as I hid in my room upstairs. "She should have the chance to find out who she wants to be and what she wants to do!"

"She'll make a beautiful wife." My father's tone was final. My mother grew silent. But I imagined her expression, the tight line her lips formed, the way her eyes narrowed. I shut my door.

The fire never left my mother. She spent her entire existence fighting, taking a stand "against the man who thinks we're too fragile to be in the real world!" We attended more marches and protests together, lied to my father, and said we had errands to run and dresses to buy. I think now that he knew where we ran off to every time. He never said it; he did not have to. He knew better than to try to tame my mother.

"Do you know why I named you Joan?" she asked me one evening after my father had switched off the news channel, but only after he had scoffed about the most recent teach-in held downtown earlier that evening.

I shook my head, afraid to open my mouth and slice through the thick, suffocating tension in the air. I had a feeling she was going to attribute my name to something other than my father's sister, Joan, which was the story I had been told when I asked about my name for a family tree project in the fifth grade.

"Joan of Arc." My mother smiled at me. "She was a warrior. She fought for her country. As a woman. Better than most of the men on the battlefield, as well. Saved her country from ruins. Do you know how she was repaid?" She did not give me time to answer, assuming this was my first history lesson on French politics. "Called a witch and burned alive."

I watched my father's jaw clench and unclench, a sign of his dwindling patience. He flipped the page of his newspaper. He did not comment.

"It's not just about the big rebellions though, Joan, it's the little ones that count too. Like here in Ohio." She gestured to the television set now completely blank. "Like the protests and rallies to fight for what is right." Her eyes filled with water. She looked away before I could see a tear fall.

I am not as strong or passionate as my mother. I do not have that same fire burning deep within, setting anything I touch ablaze. I am not like Joan of Arc. I am no warrior. I was comfortable in my complacency. I did not want destruction and fury. I did not thrive in chaos. I liked consistency and comfort.

I never went to college. I married a nice man from my Uncle Ted's office after I had taken the job as secretary. I could feel the disappointment that saturated my mother's slim frame. I quit my job when I got pregnant with my first child. I had three more. My mother and father's marriage had withered further away from love as I worked tirelessly to make a house a home. My husband, Patrick, and my father often enjoyed cigars in the den while my mother nursed her glass of red wine, and I cooked pie for dessert, a perfectly golden brown just like the recipe had suggested.

My mother tells my daughter, Violet, the tales of her rebellious past. The factory line, the protests and rallies.

"It's going to be a woman's world, Violet," my mother says in that familiar, comfortable way. She speaks as if it is the first time Violet has heard these stories, as if I don't tell her these tales before she goes to bed, my own type of fairytale, in the hope that Violet is strong enough to become the warrior my mother always wanted me to be. I can see it, I can see it in her eyes as she watches the boys play outside and she is forced to sit still in her pretty dress, with her hair smoothed down in a perfect way.

"My beautiful girl," my husband will say as he kisses her cheek.

"I want to be more than beautiful," she says to me after I tell her the stories of her grandmother, the true heroine. "I want to be more than beautiful."

"It's going to be a woman's world, Violet," I say as I kiss her forehead. The same flicker flashes in her eye, a look I know all too well, the one that glimmered and shone from my mother's face as she held my hand tightly, her fist in the air, chanting along with the crowd that wanted so badly to see change.

"It's going to be a woman's world."

IRONING TO WIBG, 1965

Wendy McVicker

when rock 'n' roll was
the language of the tribe, and we
all shimmied to the same tunes,
bebopped through the same chores,
swinging on an endless loop
of melting afternoons.

The creaking board, steam
meeting steam, scent of heated
cotton and tobacco, Roy
Orbison crooning
soft and low, lifting

the ivy-filtered light
and turning it
inside-out, late-night
smoky cool—

My bare arm sweeping
back and forth, up and down, smoke
from illicit cigarettes pricking

lips, throat, lungs

opening up to sing *oh baby*—

I would grab the world,

fold it end to end

and make it sizzle

"Ironing to WIBG" is included in Wendy McVicker's chapbook, *Sliced Dark*, a collaborative project with artist John McVicker

1968

Wendy McVicker

The women

wear bikinis, and the men

cross their arms over their chests.

What are they afraid of?

One curly-haired fellow

in faded cutoffs gestures,

lectures. The young

spread out around him

like a picnic—succulent

women, lean and tangy men.

That was the year

I commenced—

gave up virginity, rode out

into the wide world.

Only it wasn't so wide,

back then. Women

sat on the grass,

men stood. One

man lectured,

then another.

The women laughed
into their hands,
or looked away, sultry
in a cloud of smoke.
Not changed much
since Austen's day, still
all subtle bargaining
and backroom deals.
But it was about to.
And maybe those men,
the ones with their arms
crossed over their chests,
maybe they saw it coming.
All that power unleashed.
And theirs, draining away.

CURIOUS TIMES AND BIG BRASS BALLS

Mick Puckett

My wife and I arranged to meet our son when he left his job for the evening. We had learned online of a rally, knew the stated objectives and outcomes, knew the routing of marchers through downtown Louisville, and the estimated length of the event. We thought the cause was appropriate to introduce our willing adult offspring to his first protest march.

As we gathered with the demonstrators, and pointed out the best signs and chants, it occurred to me that this demonstration was just a tad . . . sanitized, too much like a formal lesson plan. The objective was achieved, I suppose. The interesting experience and well-made point were positive overall, but I couldn't shake the idea that something essential in the experience was missing for me. Would it feel better if . . . maybe it was something a bit more capricious and spontaneous?

I kept my feelings to myself. I, after all, came of age in a time so very different from the present. The late '60s and early '70s, in my experience, had been exciting and terrifying, spontaneous and unpredictable. The cultural upheaval, hallucinogens, the war in Vietnam, and political protests had all assaulted the collective consciousness of my generation.

————

University of Kentucky Campus, May 1970: Kent State +2.

It was a beautiful morning, one of those mornings when the spring sunshine and fresh air—cleansed of yesterday's tear gas—made a person happy to be alive. I was on the way to my anthropology final, Blue Book under my arm, with the intention of joining the ongoing student antiwar demonstrations after the test.

Kentucky wasn't exactly the hotbed of 1960s' radicalism that Governor Nunn would have had folks believe. The protest marches that spring had been exceptionally peaceful and sometimes rather enjoyable, strange considering the looming threat of the draft and the war. Since the massacre at Kent State, however, it was now so very much more personal. The demonstrations on campus had taken a turn, become a bit rowdier and much more serious. The night before, while a boisterous student rally was held at what was then the ROTC building, a suspicious fire had been started in an old warehouse across campus.

Though few were even aware of it, the burned building had a tiny, faded old sign over one door reading Air Force ROTC.

"Arson! Student Protestors Burn ROTC Building" was the large, bold headline in the *Herald Leader* the next morning. The ensuing fire had "officially" been blamed on the students, and a young woman walking close to the building had been charged with arson. (Evidence presented in the coming weeks, however, would suggest that the university had possibly taken advantage of the circumstances to "clear the space" for a new parking lot for the basketball team.)

The state police and the National Guard were mobilized to deal with the protestors and were using pepper gas, tear gas, and nightsticks with liberal (?) abandon. It was tense to say the least. Still a couple blocks from campus, I noticed the familiar squawk of a bullhorn. Things were beginning early. I turned the corner and saw a few students in the distance running from police. I wanted to be there but wasn't going to risk missing the easy final. I deliberately walked in a slightly different direction, a more direct route to the building where I'd be taking my test. Approaching a cross street next to campus, I heard a loud clomp, clomping sound and turned to see an enormous state policeman, six foot, five or six inches, riot-helmeted, and wearing a gas mask, barreling toward me at full gallop, swinging a nightstick in a circular motion over his head. Momentarily stunned by the sight, I hesitated a second or two before taking off, running as fast as I could and had almost escaped before being struck a glancing blow to the head. Thankfully, his attention was then diverted, and he sprinted toward another hapless soul walking down the sidewalk.

How very strange. This was bizarre. However much I may have "deserved" this on other occasions, I had only been walking to school with long hair for the sole purpose of taking my exam. I sat on the sidewalk, still a bit dazed, feeling a large knot rising on the back of my head, and I flinched as someone approached muttering from behind. I turned toward the voice.

"What? Sorry, I didn't hear you."

A middle-aged man with dark, close-cropped hair, a prominent beer gut and bloody "wife-beater" T-shirt walked up beside me, bleeding from a gash in his forehead.

"Jeesus H. Christ! I saw that big sumbitch comin' at me with that club and my asshole drawed up, just drawed up tight! That ever happen to you, boy?"

"Can't say I've ever really thought about it, but it sounds reasonable."

This guy looked like the biggest redneck I'd ever seen, a lot like some of the crazies who'd come into town from Winchester or Mount Sterling to beat up the longhairs on a Friday night, someone who I would run from on a normal evening. Head wound notwithstanding, he was also bleeding profusely from his ear.

I took off my shirt and handed it to him.

"Here, you need to take care of your head and ear."

He absently took my T-shirt, sat down beside me, and dabbed at his head, seemingly surprised at how much he was bleeding.

"Hey, boy, you got a hell of a goose egg sproutin' up through all that hair."

He gave me a friendly shove. My head was really getting sore.

"I heard how ya'll're tryin' to stop that goddamn war and came to join up with ya." He offered me his bloody hand. "I'm Ray, Ray Sizemore. My boy's over there now, and I ain't never been so scared in my life. All our young'uns are dyin' over them Viet Congs that ain't done nothin' to any of us. We gotta stop that foolish shit."

"I couldn't agree more, Ray." I turned and noticed the tears. Ray was beginning to quietly sob, not from the terrible beating he'd just taken; that was nothing compared to the anguish he was feeling about his son. "I love my boy . . . love my boy." He accented the words "love" and "boy."

It was curious, how experiencing something as random and insane as that morning's events could suddenly humanize a complete stranger, bypassing all the political or philosophical or cultural obstructions that normally divide people. He had let me in, given me a small glimpse into his soul with his short statement. I suddenly felt as connected, as close to Ray as to anyone I knew, and my heart was absolutely breaking for him. By the time we had cleaned each other up, exchanged addresses, and headed our separate ways, I wondered if we'd ever meet again. Life tends to be cruel that way more often than not. I'd missed my exam by that point, and my head was throbbing—the result of my earlier attempt to avoid trouble.

This time my choice was different. I headed in the direction of the student center where the climax to the week's demonstrations was underway. Two lines formed along an open lawn at the edge of the campus—the National Guard and state police in gas masks and riot gear on one side and the students on the other. The National Guardsmen, I noticed, were just a bunch of frightened kids, most of them our age. Actually, they were just like us, except they had families with enough money or political clout to avoid the draft by joining the swollen ranks of the National Guard. Oh, but they were armed, and they were frightened, and after the Kent State killings, it seemed that "a reasonable and appropriate response" had been taken off the table. The state police were itching for a fight; they'd worn gas masks and body armor for a couple of very warm days and were surely sick of taking shit from a bunch of hippie kids.

The student protesters were surprisingly peaceful, but in all fairness, had been shouting and chanting some rather rude and unkind things at the opposition, resulting in a complete standoff. This day, however, under orders from the governor, the National Guardsmen chambered live ammunition, fixed bayonets (seriously?), and announced that they would drive the students from the campus by force. The atmosphere grew more and more tense. I could actually imagine Kent State happening again. As the Guardsmen began moving forward in a line, prodding any stragglers with bayonets, someone on a bullhorn announced that the Baptist Seminary across the street had offered its huge front lawn as a refuge, and the police and National Guard did not have permission to enter their private property. This was the only way out. A thousand-plus students rushed across the street, followed by several tear-gas canisters.

For the next hour or two, the situation appeared hopeless as each side, defending territory, hurled insults and an occasional projectile across the street at their antagonists. It was very faint at first.

That sound, was it music? No, it couldn't be, just random sounds carried by the breeze. Wait, there it was again, a vaguely familiar sound, but what? Over a span of two or three minutes, the sound wafted in and out until finally, it struck the ear with more definition. Yes, there it was . . . a calliope? What in the world? A calliope playing "The Wheels on the Bus Go Round and Round." Seriously? Whoa, maybe that last joint was a bit over the line.

As the music got louder, we finally spotted the source. No way, this couldn't be happening. A Mr. Softy ice cream truck turned from a small side street onto blocked-off Limestone Street, recorded music blaring from a horn-shaped speaker on its roof. It drove directly between the two warring factions and slowly pulled into the driveway of the seminary, the driver, joint in mouth, waving at the crowd. The situation, having hovered in the dire-to-hopeless crisis mode for hours was suddenly defused and quickly turned into an all-inclusive party.

Crisis was averted as everyone on both sides of the street broke ranks and loaded up on Mr. Softy ice cream. Students, state police, National Guardsmen, everyone was suddenly beginning to mix together; later, even sharing a large Ho Chi Minh birthday sheet-cake brought by some students. The powder keg had been smothered in soft-whip ice cream, thanks to the brassiest of balls and utterly stoned countenance of the enterprising young businessman whose risky decision had paid off handsomely.

I actually did see my new friend Ray (he of the drawed-up asshole) once more a couple of weeks later at a rally. He'd lost the hearing in the ear that had been bleeding so profusely from the beating he took, but Ray was ecstatic. He had just heard from his son who'd been wounded in Nam.

"What a godsend," said Ray. "My boy is coming home!"

I TRY TO THINK OF THE SHOCKING EVENT

Christine Telfer

*"There's a shocking event for every generation, when everyone remembers where they were and what they were doing. It was Pearl Harbor for the World War II generation; for you [*a poet who'd presented a poem about 9/11*], it was 9/11; for others, it was the Kennedy assassination."*
—Comment in a poetry workshop

for my generation, born in the wake
of the Kennedy assassination, his brother's
death the first historical event I remember.

(That MLK was shot in '68, too, though
I don't remember hearing of it on the news
may say something about how much coverage

he got on the mainstream channels my parents
watched, or me, and what caught my attention
at three or four, but that may be another story . . .)

What I do remember, later on, were broadcasts
from Vietnam, starving children, sometimes
bombs going off right in front of us on screen

while we were eating.

Then Nixon, the mess of Watergate
(I wouldn't hear about Kent State until a little
later) but do remember those stickers

with the w's blocked off, so they read
Nixon No! instead of *Now*, and how our
president said he wasn't a crook though

even I knew better.

Clemente killed in an airplane crash.
While flying off to help. Victims of an
earthquake. On New Year's Eve.

Okay. That was a shock. But not a big
enough one to rock an entire generation—
not everyone's a Pirates fan.

I had only just become one.

Heroes died. Our country was horrid.
That's how I remember seeing things.
Of course, there was always music.

Then John Lennon. Killed. The same year
I first fell. In love. Very shocking. But *nowhere*
near as much as my loved one's touch was.

Tiananmen square, the Berlin wall falling.
I wasn't sure, at first, what to make of it all.
The USSR fell apart while I was teaching

abroad in Bulgaria. Was I glad?
Or in a way a little bit sad?

A bigger shock, for me: sometime around
then I met someone. I thought might shock
my life forever. He didn't.

A few years later, I met another.

And then in the '90s, America was shining
bright—kind of surprising—almost like we
were the *only* country. In the new global reality.

I sometimes worried about the rest of the world.

And God knows, we were far from perfect.
Oklahoma City was shocking then; now
it'd be just one more bombing . . .

When W. got in without winning more
of the popular vote than Gore, I thought,
well, that's how it goes. *Was I beginning to see*

the two major parties as Coke/Pepsi?

Then 9/11 happened. Somehow, I wasn't
shocked. I knew other countries still hated
US. After that, the whole mess of Iraq,

and the fact that we couldn't stop it—
despite so many protests and oh, you know—
no weapons of mass destruction discovered—

it was all far too long and drawn out to be . . .
though each civilian beheading was certainly   *(Kenneth Bigley. Margaret Hassan)*

(James Foley

a shock   *a few years later)*

So very troubling. I remember thinking
that W'd probably go down in history
as the worst president, *ever*, but . . .

In a world where there's just been
One shock after another   *Sandy Hook. The Boston Marathon.*
I never thought . . .   *A church in Charleston. The Paris attacks.*
                                                 Another shooting in Charlotte . . .
                                                 the list goes on . . .

We'd end up with *Trump!* But *he's*

not the shock; what we've become is.

Mass shooting quotidian. Is the stock market   *Las Vegas. Parkland*

God?   *What's next?*

I shouldn't have asked.   *The Tree of Life.*

And this one happened here.

So that's it—the shocking event—

for Pittsburgh.

There doesn't seem to be a single   *too many to count*

One. Each of us has our own. Shock.

For me, it's my brother's death

which has nothing to do with any of this

As each school, each city, each church or synagogue,

Club or concert hall becomes some kind of battleground.

Or just a walk to the store. If you're a black male in a hoodie.

The only event that would shock us all—

a nuclear war   *and who'd be left to remember?*

BOOMER RETROSPECTIVE

Leslie Smith Townsend

We slander millennials, as if they were one
fabric and held no ethic of concern and protest,

forgetting we were once so self-absorbed, as if
our revolution of free love secured *our* transformation.

How long did we stand by decrees
of just and simpler living? We sold

our backwoods farms, played to corporate values,
and what remains—the detritus of our greed—

parking lots, power plants, megastores,
we leave to those we blame for being selfish.

Excuse me, but weren't we also young
with dreams aplenty?

We thought our generation was the first
to seek redemption of the ills

left by our forbearers—sexism, racism, all
the isms and destruction of the earth.
We wept and whined without a glance
toward those who'd gone before so we'd be free

to choose our way—arrogance, stunning,
as only youth can be. And yet, we busted barriers

of exclusion and narrow-mindedness
like junkyard dogs, at times, but still,

prophecy is seldom gentle and, in the end,
I give thanks for the bull-headedness of youth,

the shake up, break up, make up
that yields a better world.

DANCING FOR EQUAL RIGHTS

Nancy Wick

It was Sharon's idea to hold the fundraising dance for the Equal Rights Amendment. The question was, would anyone come? After all, this was Evansville, Indiana—an industrial hub in the southwestern corner of the state fronting the Ohio River where, I often joked, only 50 liberals lived. None of us sitting on the floor of the Unitarian Fellowship—a.k.a., liberal central—were sure what the outcome of such a dance would be. Yet, our intrepid band of 10 feminists was determined to do what we could to support the ERA's passage.

It was 1977, and the ERA was wending its torturous way across the country. The amendment stated: "Equality of rights under the law shall not be denied or abridged by the United States or by any state on account of sex." *Well, duh,* I thought. *You mean that isn't the law already?* Sadly, it was not. I'd grown up in a world where women could not get credit in their own names, weren't admitted to the country's most elite universities or any of the military academies, and sometimes had to get their husband's permission to have their tubes tied.

Things had only recently begun to change, as the women's movement gained momentum during my college years in the late 1960s. Congress had passed the ERA in 1972, but that was just the first step. It had to be ratified by three-fourths—that's 38—of the states. *No sweat,* I thought. *Surely this is a no-brainer.* And at first, that seemed to be true, as 30 states got on board by the end of 1973. But then opposing forces mounted a devastating attack, and only five more states had signed on since then. Our group watched in horror as our own state senate became deadlocked on the issue, 25 to 25. The amendment squeaked through only after President-elect Jimmy Carter's wife Rosalyn made a last-minute phone call to a single wavering Indiana senator.

Now Sharon was urging us to financially support the campaign for ratification—and have some fun, too. She elaborated on her suggestion of a fund-raising dance: "We'll call it the Bra Burner's Ball."

The idea of bra-burning originated in 1968, when a group of women had protested the Miss America Pageant, tossing female items, including bras, into a "freedom trashcan," but nobody actually burned a bra. It was afterward, when a reporter drew an analogy between these protests and men burning their draft cards, that the headline, "Bra burners at Miss America" created a label that stuck. Since then, the term had been used to ridicule feminists. (Okay, a lot of us weren't wearing bras in the 1970s, but we hadn't felt it necessary to burn them.)

"I don't want to be associated with that stupid term," I piped up.

"Well then, a dance by some other name," Sharon countered.

"Where would we have it?"

"Who would provide the music?"

"How would we get people to come?"

Everyone was talking at once.

The 10 of us had formed a consciousness-raising group a couple of years before. CR groups, as they were called, provided a forum at which women could discuss matters that, in the past, they had kept to themselves. We talked about everything from how we felt about menstruating and being whistled at on the street to getting illegal abortions and being raped. The group bred solidarity, a sense that one was not alone with one's challenges, especially those we faced because we were women. The fact that we ranged in age from mid-20s to mid-50s allowed younger members to learn about the bad old days. I admired our elder members, one of whom had started the group.

We knew we were a minority in our town. When I'd arrived there for my first job after college, this is what I'd found: Almost everyone I met was married, and the wives seemed content with the status quo. Women who worked outside the home still did all the cooking and cleaning and most of the child care, never doubting that this was the way it would always be. Yet, if I brought up the topic of sexism, they didn't see it as a problem. At the hospital where I got my first job, doctors were overwhelmingly male, nurses overwhelmingly female, and the doctors were gods. When I took a new job at the local newspaper, I found a mostly male staff who—upon discovering that I was a feminist—took delight in teasing me. The guys groused loudly when an edict came down from management (the paper was owned by a national chain) aiming to root out sexism from news stories. Even female leaders in the town could come across as conservative. Once, I attended a conference on women in business, and one of the speakers—an officer at a local bank—had begun her talk with "I'm not a feminist, but . . ."

So, the idea that we could draw a crowd to a dance with a feminist theme didn't seem too promising. It all might have died right there, if Sharon hadn't been behind it.

"Listen," she said, "we can do this. There's not that much goes on in this town. People will want to come, just as something different to do."

Sharon was petite—probably not more than five feet two—with light brown hair, mischievous blue eyes behind glasses, and a curly perm. What she lacked in stature she made up for in pure chutzpah. As a social worker, she had talked her way into a newly created post as counselor for the local police, which made her practically the only woman who worked in an organization about as macho as it gets. If anyone could make such a dance happen, she could.

"We need something more as a draw," I said.

Sharon grinned. "We'll have a beauty contest . . . for men."

I smirked. "We'll call it Mr. Heavensville."

The room erupted in laughter and overlapping ideas:

"We'll have the contestants wear sashes, like in Miss America."

"We'll have a talent contest . . . "

"And an interview with stupid questions."

"But where are we going to find the men to do this?"

Our youngest member was sure her husband—who had a wry sense of humor—would find the idea hilarious, another suggested a work colleague, a third her friend. Together we came up with a list of five or six men we thought would be willing to be silly for a good cause, or to please the women in their lives. Then Sharon had another brainstorm.

"We should have waiters dressed as Playboy Bunnies."

"Who would ever be willing to do that?" I asked.

"Oh, I know some fraternity guys at the University of Evansville," she said with a sly smile.

Sharon was a graduate of the small, private college whose perennially strong basketball team the whole town rooted for. She knew, she told us, that one campus fraternity sponsored an annual Miss Watermelon Bust contest. "They have a social obligation to redeem themselves by providing us with bunnies."

I didn't know how she would get the frat boys to see it that way, but if anyone could . . .

Slowly, it all came together. Playing on the initials of the amendment and the word "era," we called it the New ERA Ball. We divided up the tasks— finding a hall to rent and a disk jockey for the music, making decorations, arranging for refreshments, getting some publicity (which—since I worked at a newspaper—was my job). We would charge admission and sell snacks to raise money.

The men we asked to be in the beauty contest laughed and said yes (maybe they were just a little bit flattered). Sharon wrote to the fraternity making exactly the argument she'd made to us, wisely adding that the bunnies—with the skimpy attire we planned—would likely be hustled by women attendees and earn tips. And amazingly, the guys were persuaded, maybe because they liked the idea of participating in something outrageous. The venue and the DJ were found. My newspaper carried a brief story announcing the event but did not want to cover it. The entertainment editor and the metro editor rolled their eyes at the suggestion. (I had no success selling tickets to the newspaper staff, either—they chuckled and made cracks about how they didn't want to be mobbed by a bunch of angry women's libbers.) Luckily, I knew a woman at the competing newspaper who loved the idea; she promised to send a reporter and photographer.

We dressed the waiters in white short-shorts and pink tank tops, with the requisite ears, cuffs, and tails. We stopped short, however, at requiring the four-inch spike heels real bunnies at the Playboy clubs were required to wear. The beauty contestants—most of whom came in suits and ties—wore sashes adorned with glitter. For the winner we had a mangy, fur-trimmed robe, a crown, and a bouquet of plastic flowers.

To keep the contest short and sweet, we decided that the talent portion would show off all the men at once, which we did by having them link arms and do an enthusiastic, if unimpressive, chorus-line kick to the tune of a song they sang together. The interview section consisted of one provocative question, for example: "You find yourself suddenly broke. Would you sell your body to buy groceries?" To judge the contest, we had made an "applause meter" out of cardboard. We would ask the audience to applaud for each contestant and we would move the needle the appropriate amount.

When the night of the ball arrived, I approached the venue—a small rented hall in the basement of a building—with trepidation. Despite the excitement of the planning, I still worried that nobody would come. My date was a handsome man I'd recently met in an art appreciation class, and I didn't want to feel embarrassed if the evening proved a flop.

The room was nearly empty when we arrived, which did not bode well. I greeted my CR group colleagues, and my date and I pitched in with the setup, arranging long tables in rows and leaving a space up front for the dance floor. I noticed the DJ setting up his equipment off to one side. Sharon was helping the fraternity boys with their bunny accessories, and they were punching each other's arms, shaking their cottontails, and posing like models, clearly covering up nervousness with bravado. The Mr. Heavensville contestants talked quietly to each other.

Then people started trickling in—a few at first, followed by larger groups, until the space filled, and the dance floor became crowded. Who were all these people? Friends of CR group members? Friends of friends? ERA supporters? Maybe Evansville's closeted liberals—more numerous than I realized—were crawling out of their hiding places to show their true colors for this one special night. In the end I didn't care; they were here, and that was all that mattered. As the evening progressed, the bunnies circulated, offering to fetch food and mixers (it was BYOB) and the women fawned over them. I caught Sharon's eye and smiled; everyone was having fun.

Then the contest started. The men—who knew the interview questions in advance—had all prepared witty answers that drew laughter from the onlookers, who clapped rhythmically when the contestants did their chorus line routine. The winner, a slender, middle-aged, balding friend of mine, pretended to wipe away a tear as he received his crown and took his triumphal walk through the crowd. When it was all over, the CR group stayed behind to clean up, marveling to each other about how well it had all gone. And the next day, when the big article with several photos appeared in the paper, we couldn't resist calling each other to celebrate.

After paying our expenses, we cleared a little over three hundred dollars—not bad for an event organized by a small group of women with little experience at such things. We sent the money to the ratification campaign. I also sent a brief essay describing the dance to *MS Magazine*. But they received a lot of such items in those dizzying days when the campaign for ratification was in full swing, and they didn't use mine. I was gratified, however, to receive a kind, handwritten note from one of the editors thanking us for the submission and adding, "Sounds like fun!"

We sponsored the dance three subsequent years, though none was quite as exciting as the original. In spite of our efforts, the ERA was never ratified, thanks mostly to the efforts of Phyllis Schlafly and her STOP ERA movement (the STOP stood for "stop taking our privileges"). Schlafly claimed to represent full-time housewives—those she said would lose privileges—even though she was a lawyer, newsletter editor, touring speaker, and political activist.

The champion of her message in Indiana was Sen. Joan Gubbins, R-Indianapolis, the leading opponent of the ERA in the state senate. She forecasted the measure would lead to homosexual marriage, sexual deviancy, female soldiers, and motherless children. It turned out she was half right, but not because of the ERA.

Since then I've lived to see many improvements in the status of women in the United States, though those improvements are always under threat. That's why I'm encouraged to see renewed efforts to get the ERA ratified. Maybe a new generation of women—living in a more enlightened world—will succeed where we failed.

I don't live in Evansville anymore, but Sharon—feisty as ever—still does. Is she up for organizing another New ERA Ball? If anyone could pull it off . . .

RED AND YELLOW, BLACK AND WHITE

Teresa Willis

"Jesus loves the little children
all the children of the world
red and yellow
black and white
they are precious in His sight
Jesus loves the little children of the world."
                    —Clarence Woolston

he had a dream and
it seems like a fine one to me
but facts are sketchy
about this new dead guy
my third-grade teacher said:
"he was good for the coloreds
but now he's dead"

I wonder where the yellow children live
how odd they must look
with their Crayola-defined skin

I line up my crayons:
red and yellow, black and white
why doesn't the song mention the flesh-colored children
all the kids I know are flesh-colored

he had a dream
he tells us about it
right before the war footage
and the casualty count

he entrances me
he was a preacher
I love this new dead guy
because he was like Jesus
killed by the bad guys
'cause he was too good

the library had nothing
of him or his dream
my mystified parents
consent to a book order
a freshly minted biography
offered though the church

I read the book and learn
that flesh-colored people are white

that colored people are black
and that his death
is the saddest thing
I've ever known

From an unpublished play, *Eenie Meanie*, by Teresa Willis

COMING
OF AGE

———⟨∘⟩———

"The coming-of-age story has sort of become a joke. It's something to capitalize on, and that is painful because when you are coming of age—when you are going through something like that—the genre is so meaningful."

—Mae Whitman

JACKIE PATTERSON
SAVED US

Sheila Carter-Jones

The Reverend Mothers and Sisters said,
On turning sixteen, you should believe
you are woman enough to clean
the rich lady's house, responsible enough
to pick up after grown folks who
have money enough
to afford sloppiness.

On turning sixteen, you should believe
you are strong enough to heave
a two-gallon pail of water, wring a mop
resting on hips enough and dare not
spill a drop, then on knees enough, wax
the floor enough to see the shadow
of your beauty.

And we believed until she came
like a prophet walking on water. Or,

call it beginners' luck, maybe, just
plain fat rat getting over.
Whatever it was, Jackie Patterson saved
like Jesus wouldn't have done
if we just believed what we were told
when we turned sixteen.

It was the way Jackie swaggered
from the country squire after
her first day of bucket work.
Under the striped cotton dress,
she wore six pair of panties, all silk
and lace from the rich lady's chest
of drawers and as she shed them
in the living room we oohed and awed,
reached for flowers in meadows,
ribbons, flying fairies,

and the very next day,
the rich lady came for her undies and we
all laughed when Jackie claimed innocence
said she just wanted to try them on,
she really did intend to bring them back.

We weren't sorry when she handed over
silky pinks, blues, violets, and white ones

so white, not white-gray like ours.
And all summer long we loved her
like a goddess—sneaked gifts
of chocolate kisses, Wise potato chips,
and Mission grape pop through Jackie's
window because we knew, she saved us
before we turned sixteen.

TELLING HER WHOLE LIFE

Kari Gunter-Seymour

Twilight's blue breeze, curtains lift,
her teenage body reflected in the panes.

Stomach muscles cinched,
yearning thinner thighs, she sets

arm to turntable, sways, holds hands
with an invisible boy, an audience

of forgotten dolls peeks through slats
on her bedroom closet door.

Spiraling deep into the musk of her body,
the ache of swallowed starlight an abeyance,

her super power—to sit on the edge
of the bed, listen to the world spin,

vinyl on a player,
killing her softly.

THE FERN BAR

Ginny Horton

"Double double," Vernon hollered as he walked into the Old Mule Tavern. The wooden door slammed behind him. I was wiping down the mahogany bar with a damp bar rag. Without looking up, I could see him in his overalls, limping slightly, white hair standing up on his scalp like a rooster's comb.

"Well, good mornin' to you too, darlin'," I said. It was 5:00 a.m. on a Thursday, and Vernon was getting ready to go to work down in a coal mine in Parkersburg, West Virginia. He hiked his leg over the round bar stool and fell into his slump.

I grabbed one of the gimlet glasses still warm from the dishwasher, filled it with the cracked ice I had just put into the aluminum sink and reached for the Jim Beam behind me.

"You still here?" he barked.

I swung my long hair over my shoulder to get it out of my face. "Yes, sir, unless you got me confused with some other smart-ass tends bar here."

As I poured the whiskey, its deep sweetness rose and blended with the aroma of fresh coffee in the air-conditioned air.

"When you goin', smart-ass?" he asked as I placed his drink down.

"I ain't sure."

"You ain't goin'," he said.

Vernon took a swig and laid his big paw in front of him. The moon of his fingernails seemed to mock the coal dust that darkened their square tips. After a couple more JBs, he'd be his same sullen self. Four more guys just like him, only younger and scrawnier, would be in shortly and want the same thing. I left the bottle and glasses on the bar top and went to cook their eggs.

The Old Mule used to be a dive bar and restaurant; one of my townie friend's parents had recently saved it from the wrecking ball, God knows why. Her mom was a country club do-gooder who knew nothing about business and even less about her clientele. I think her husband thought it was a good idea. He could have the bar he always wanted, and she could impress her friends with her business savvy, such as it was, and they could make money at the same time. We called her "Proud Mary," like the Credence song but never to her face.

The locals now called the Old Mule a "fern bar," which was as insulting as they could get. I guess Proud Mary thought she was onto something. It always made me laugh at how preposterous the whole thing was. I could see her in a macramé class at the country club, making plant hangers for the bar as if it were her favorite charity. They hung from the ceiling and the regulars blew cigarette smoke into their bottoms, which made almost everyone feel a little better. It felt like a perfectly good dive bar with the shit kicked out of it.

The grill was heating up, and I disappeared through the swinging door to the kitchen. I opened the walk-in for eggs and bacon. The heavy door coughed and expelled its frosty breath, which always felt good later in the day when the kitchen would be hot and stinky with grease and sweat. I came in here all day long just to clear my head. I didn't grow up in this town like everyone else here, but I knew it was time for me to leave. The regulars would think it was because of Proud Mary, but they would be wrong. I knew if I didn't leave now, I'd be stuck here for the rest of my life. I'm not saying that's bad, it's just something I gotta do.

I carried the bacon and eggs out of the walk-in as the heavy door slammed behind me. Phyllis was on her way in. I heard her toss her car keys into her bag and smelled her Avon cologne. I imagined the lines her sponge curlers had left in her hair. I could never figure out why someone would curl their dead, old, dried-up, cotton-candy hair to stand over a steaming hot grill all day.

"Hey, Princess," I hollered to Phyllis as I cracked Vernon's eggs on the side of a bowl and poured them out of their shells. They hissed onto the hot grill with the bacon.

"You still here?" Phyllis came through the swinging door.

"Hell, yeah," I said as if she were the reason I hadn't yet left.

Phyllis pulled an apron on over her bowling ball of a body and picked eight pieces of white bread out of a long loaf and dealt them into the toaster.

A car pulled into the gravel parking lot.

"There's the Boss Man," Phyllis said. He was Proud Mary's husband, Mark. Phyllis called him Boss Man because he was so pussy-whipped.

She painted melted butter on the toast and cut it diagonally, which was another thing I could never understand. Proud Mary thought it was fancy. Not fancy like having your hair look like you'd slept on toilet-paper rolls overnight. "They'll think it tastes better. Trust me," she actually said.

I slid Vernon's fried eggs onto a plate with a spatula. Added the bacon. Phyllis put a triangular stack of toast on a plate while I plated another breakfast.

As I backed through the swinging doors, a full plate in each hand, Vernon was already sitting at a table with his buddies. I placed his breakfast in front of him and the other in front of his nephew across from him. When I started working here, Phyllis warned me that the miners ate the same thing every day and wanted it at the same time, so they never ordered their food.

I came back with two trays of bacon and eggs for the rest of the table. Mark stood next to it with his coffee.

"What's wrong with this country is there's no respect for the working man. Them mining companies use arbitration against every one of you. Ninety percent of your grievances don't even matter; there's no penalty, they just pay the arbitrators and fire ya'll." He took a sip and realized no one was listening. He pitied the miners and it made them hate him.

I placed one of the trays on a tray table and, holding the other tray, set their plates down in front of them. Vernon tucked his checkered napkin into the top of his overalls.

"Well, I'll let ya'll eat," Mark said. He put his hand on Vernon's shoulder.

"Git along, then," Vernon said.

Phyllis and I usually sat down with a cup a coffee before it got busy. She glanced up at the clock over the swinging door.

"Sandra's late again. C'mon, Diana, looks like we're doin' setup."

I grabbed bundles of the cheap flatware we had rolled up inside checkered napkins at the end of the day yesterday. Phyllis was already wiping down the matching oilcloth table covers.

"Donny came in last night," I said as I set the table. Phyllis looked up at me and paused, the dishrag hanging from her hand. Donny was Sandra's truck-driving husband and whenever he got back in town, there was hell to pay in one way or another, and for our part, it meant making sure Sandra kept her job.

An hour later, Sandra showed up with her shades on. We sorta knew there'd be a big shiner still purple and running up the side of her pink nose. She was crying and we were used to that.

The coal miners shook their heads. Phyllis got a steak from the walk-in to put over Sandra's souvenir from her husband, and we tried to get her calm before Proud Mary came in and started acting outraged. She'd give Sandra the telephone number of a shelter and a warning that she'd fire her if it kept up, but what Sandra really wanted was the day off.

We sat down to cigarettes and coffee before getting hit with the lunch crowd.

"I ain't going back this time," Sandra said. Phyllis and I looked at each other ready to roll our eyes but stopped because maybe, just maybe we prayed, this time she was serious.

"Was he drunk?" Phyllis asked. We knew he was, but it was an easy way to get Sandra to spill.

"God, yes, he was drunk, hopped up on speed. We went dancin' down at Harpo's; it was shot night, and we got into the Jack Daniels. Two for one." She pulled a cigarette from her vinyl cigarette case and snapped it shut.

"Was it crowded?" I asked as I lit her cigarette.

"Yeah. Billy Moss was there with Cayla."

Phyllis and I smiled because they were so cute together.

"We closed the place and hung out in the parking lot smokin' reefer, and Billy Moss come up and asked me if I could score any speed for him." She blew smoke out of her nostrils. "I give him about five of Donny's Black Beauties. Donny's always given Billy drugs. I didn't think it was no big deal." She took another puff before resting the cigarette on her saucer.

"So this morning, Donny's counting his stash and wants to know what I done with his stuff and I told him and . . ." As Sandra looked down, her blonde hair fell like a protective curtain around her face. "He went nuts on me. Called me a stupid cow."

Phyllis put her flabby arm around Sandra's shoulders. I put my head back and blew smoke into the bottom of a fern. I knew her face hurt something awful, but the name calling seemed to hurt Sandra worse. It was like the shiner just popped up on her face in response to his words.

"Bastard prick," seemed like the best I could do. My stomach hurt from too much coffee.

Proud Mary's ferns looked like they were trying to climb out of their macramé hangers. I looked out the window as a couple of pickups pulled in. A big rig hauling coal groaned down the highway.

We put Sandra behind the bar where the regulars were used to her. The younger guys would offer to kick Donny's ass "all the way to Memphis." Someone else would offer her a place to stay and she'd say she'd think about it. Sometimes she stayed with Phyllis until Donny went out trucking again, but when he came back, it would start again.

At lunch, I waited tables. I liked the folks who came in, especially the guys from the printer's shop. We were all in our early 20s and flirted with each other. It didn't mean nothing. It's just something we did.

"You still goin' to Key West?" Wesley, the tall one always asked as if I changed my mind daily.

"Ain't nothing but a bunch of tourists," one of the others would say and they all would shake their heads over their beers. Today was no different.

"Key West is an island, in case you ain't got a map. It's got beaches all the way around it." I knew they didn't believe I would go. Nobody could have a dream around here without everybody stompin' on it.

Some country people came in and didn't say much. It made me sad that lunch at the Old Mule was their idea of something special. I wanted to send Sandra home with them as if putting her out in the fields would nourish her. Their big bodies and heavy worn clothes held a gravity that made them sit quietly as if waiting for a hall clock to tick off another hour of their lives.

Dr. Barnes came in and ate a chef's salad. Phyllis got him to take a professional peek at Sandra's eye. He put some ice in a towel and told us to make sure she sat down and kept her eye covered with it. Phyllis put the steak on a plate.

Mr. Petersen from the bank, shaking from the palsy, spilled his coffee all over his table. As I wiped it up, he smiled from under his graying mustache.

"Heard you was leavin' town," he said.

"Yes, sir. I'm ready to get outta here and do something, see something, be something." I knew I sounded ridiculous.

"Where you gonna do all this good stuff?"

"Key West," I said as if everyone went there.

"You a Hemingway fan?"

"Yes, but that's not why I chose it."

"Ah, gotta boyfriend waitin'?" He stirred a shot of Bailey's into his coffee.

"No, sir." I grinned. "I just feel like if I stay here, I'll miss something."

"Like what?" He looked at me over his glasses.

"My life," I said, not intending to sound like a smart-ass. "My car's already paid for. All I got to do is get in it and go."

He raised his coffee and said, "Then, let nothing stop you from following your dreams."

I looked down at my greasy running shoes. I was tired of being made to feel guilty for leaving. The folks here took it as an insult.

"I know what you're thinking, but I've got things to do there." I waited for him to meet my eyes, but he kept drinking his coffee. I started to walk away.

"Diana," he said.

I turned and his eyes were sad.

"It's a shame," he said. "That you have to go."

In the next booth, someone I didn't know had gotten knocked up and ordered slices of apple and blueberry pie for dessert. The customer then handed me quarters for the jukebox. I chose Marshall Tucker's "Heard it in a Love Song" and some Allman Brothers. They were good for my daydreaming: they understood I needed to leave, and I understood the ramblin' man's heart.

After the lunch crowd thinned out, Phyllis and I cleaned the grill, scraping up all the greasy bits with a razor blade. We scoured it with steel wool and squirted lemons on it and their smell rose up fresh as green grass. I went back out to the dining room and wiped down the tables and picked up my tips left between salt and pepper shakers or slid under sugar jars. Mr. Petersen left his business card under a five-dollar bill and I put the money in my pocket.

A tableful of guys from Lester's Body Shop was still drinking beer. Pure Prairie League's "Amy" routed itself along the familiar track in our brains. I saw myself on a pier at sunset, singing along with a crowd that played guitars or tambourines, some with harmonicas in their mouths, and feeling a part of something big and new. We didn't have tourists much in eastern Ohio, but I figured if I could deal with coal miners, I could deal with tourists.

Proud Mary came in and said, "Good afternoon," like it was. She went right to the cash register and got the cash and receipts ready for Mark to take to the bank. She was in her tennis whites and her footies had pink pompoms on the back. She swung her visor around her wrist as she headed for the walk-in. Sandra was out on break.

Proud Mary came back into the dining room. "I need to see my girls, now!" She pointed to the booth where we had our little meetings then ripped the cord from the jukebox right out of the wall. The boys from the body shop looked slapped.

"C'mon, Mary, we're paying customers. What you got against music?" Lester asked.

Mary looked sweaty from the humidity. Her bangs kinked up above her eyebrows and her mascara had smeared all the way down to her lip.

"In a minute," she snapped.

Phyllis and I sat across from each other in the sticky booth. Mary stood over us like she was waiting for our order. "Where's Sandra? And don't lie to me."

"Break," we both said.

"This can't wait," she said and lowered her voice. "Someone's stolen meat from the walk-in."

Phyllis and I inhaled.

"You serious?" Phyllis said.

"Steak." Mary raised one eyebrow.

"We serve steak?" I was genuinely surprised.

Phyllis took her hands out of her apron and placed them on the Formica. "I did take a steak out this morning and thought about using it in a lunch special." Her curls were drooping from the lunch rush.

"Six are missing. Six filet mignons from down at Kroger's." She took a breath. "About sixty dollars' worth."

Phyllis and I wrinkled our brows at each other. It was hard to feel sorry for somebody who ate ten-dollar steaks.

"Is Donny in town?" Mary asked. I could smell her deodorant; it was probably expensive, too.

Phyllis shook her head.

"I haven't seen him," I said. I heard Sandra's car door open and felt my ears get hot.

"I took the steaks, Mary," I said. I didn't want to lose my job, but I probably had the best chance of getting another one.

"Don't do this." Mary glared at me. "Everybody knows you're leaving anyway."

Sandra came in through the swinging doors from the back of the diner. The townies grew quiet and it seemed like she walked toward us in slow motion.

As she slid into the booth next to Phyllis, Mary raised her hand and slapped Sandra across the face so hard her shades fell over one ear and hung below the shiner. The sound of it shook the air.

Phyllis grabbed both of Sandra's shoulders and pulled her toward her, away from Mary. The back of her faded pink dress had darkened with sweat where she'd been sitting. Mary looked frozen with both hands over her mouth, her visor dangled from her elbow. Lester and the boys were on their feet between Mary and the table.

Sandra was bawling. Mary took a step forward and Lester took a step toward her.

"I ain't above hitting a woman," Lester said. He shook his blonde bangs out of his eyes.

Mary dropped her hands and exhaled. "Oh, get outta my way, you lily-livered asshole!"

Lester and the boys stood aside but lingered at the table.

"What I do?" Sandra looked at Mary and I wished so bad that she would just haul off and let Mary have it. But, she'd get fired for sure and thrown in jail since Mary's husband was a lawyer.

"Don't play dumb with me. You stole my steaks for you and your pitiful excuse for a husband."

"Hell, anybody in this bar coulda taken them steaks. Why you always pickin' on me?" Sandra wiped a tear away with her hammy hand.

Mary put her palms down on the table. "Listen here, Little Missy, I'm the one that's always trying to help you. I would've given you those steaks if you'd asked me."

Lester's boys went back to the bar while Lester stood guard next to Mary.

"Go sit your butt down," she demanded.

"Say, 'please,'" he said.

"Please go sit your damn butt down."

"Can I plug in the jukebox?"

"I'm trying to have a meeting here!"

"I ain't stoppin' you."

The swinging doors squeaked open. Mark came in with another man, both in polo shirts and khaki pants. Mark pointed behind him with his thumb. "We came in the back way. What the hell's going on?"

Mark's friend took a seat at the bar and faced us.

"Mary?" Mark asked.

"Sandra stole our filet mignons!" She had her hands on her hips like she was going to stomp her foot.

Mark looked around the table, stopping at Sandra who kept her head down.

"I took them steaks home last night to thaw," he said and looked at Mary as if she should've remembered.

I felt such a surge of gratitude for Mark that I went and plugged the jukebox back in. The entire bar jumped at once as a guitar chord shot through the silence. Neil Young blasted out the opening lines of "Heart of Gold." I sang along with the boys at the bar.

I slid back into the booth. Mary's ugly mouth twisted, and she looked at Sandra and I knew she was going to start apologizing in that country club formal way that made real words sound recited. Sandra would keep quiet about the slap to keep her job. Phyllis scooted back to the grill as if it were a television show she was missing.

I went to the walk-in. I felt like I'd been watching my future on TV. Like I could be poor Sandra beaten and slapped. I never thought that would happen to me before, but Sandra probably never did either. I exhaled frost like smoke. I still had Neil Young in my head. I wanted to be the person in that song. If I didn't leave, I'd never want to hear that song again.

The miners were back, dirt-tired and thirsty. They still didn't talk much. I guess it was from being down in the dark during the daylight and not seeing anything to report. Sometimes I thought the liquor made something equally dark rise up inside of them, and they had to chase it out before going down into the hole again.

I walked back behind the bar and stuck my hands in the ice. "You ever hit a woman, Vern?"

"Not unless she deserved it." His sad eyes were honest.

"What if she didn't deserve it?" I put ice in a tumbler and poured a double Jim Beam for myself and freshened up everyone else's drinks with the bottle.

"Never met a woman didn't deserve it." He gave me a serious look before grinning through his whiskers.

Mary slammed out of the dining room. Mark and his friend sat down with Phyllis and Sandra. I knew he didn't take the steaks. He was just one of those men who oozed kindness like a Boy Scout. It was his way of apologizing for having everything he had.

More townies came into the bar as it neared four o'clock. The air relaxed. I had a sudden urge for sunshine on my arms. I poured pitchers of beer and took them to the tables while Phyllis brought them fancy frosted mugs from the walk-in.

As dinner time neared, Mark nodded good-bye to everybody as he and his friend left. Phyllis, Sandra, and I sat at the bar and drank vodka with grapefruit juice while we rolled up the flatware into the checkered napkins. More folks came in after work and we gave them quarters for the jukebox and took turns tending bar and dancing.

At some point, Lester and his boys took all the ferns and put them in the toilets in the women's room and in the urinals in the men's.

"In case they need watering," Lester said with a wink.

Around ten o'clock, Phyllis, Sandra, and I got rid of the drunks and closed out the cash register. Sandra would go home with Phyllis tonight. Phyllis's husband would get mad and pout for a week. Sandra would give them a couple of the steaks.

I sat in a booth and smoked my last cigarette. An empty macramé hanger brushed against the part in my hair. I leaned back and looked up at the stupid knots. Proud Mary must've thought she was doing us all a big favor with her ropes and ferns. And probably wondered why we didn't just accept it.

I exhaled smoke. In six hours, Vernon would expect his eggs, and everything would go back to the way it was. But it would never be as good as it was today. I reckon I always knew that. I smiled. The only thing left to do . . . was go.

ON SUNDAY MORNINGS

Sheryl Loeffler

In that holy time
between Christmas and School Again,
we'd drive down white streets at daybreak—
just me and Clifford—
to open the church,
something he did every Sunday,
even when I wasn't there.

A Republican car,
an I-like-Ike Chrysler
(Ike was President
and Pius was Pope—
something a Presbyterian kid
wasn't supposed to know—
and Clifford was Clerk of Session,
world without end).

I held Clifford's hand
and jumped up the steps,
and he took out the key

and opened the door
and turned on the light,
then every light,
and lit the gas stoves—
a throwback even
for that Ohio-River-town time—
and waked the sleeping church.

Our secret church—
the silent flowers,
cold, dark, lemon-polished wood,
blue and golden light.

On Sunday mornings,
God was Clifford's,
waiting like a lover for his key,
before the church filled
with noise and life.

AT FIVE

Sheryl Loeffler

In her wheelchair, her dung heap,
crippled, shriveled, twisted,
bald, and stooped Great-Great Aunt Jemima
sits fast in her conviction, unbent in her belief
that the Lord alone heals,
that Morphine is a Devil that will not possess her,
that the *Monitor* exists for subscribing to.

Like a Medusa, like a cockatrice,
like the terrible legendary beast she is,
her glance is fatal, her half-smile paralyzes,
as if she were invented only to be
a moral example for bad little girls.

Fern! she bleats, like an unmilked goat.

Aunt Mime used to be in vaudeville,
Fern says by way of explanation.
Danced down the Mississippi on a showboat.

Fern! she bleats. And Clifford runs upstairs
to lift her out of her testimony
to God's Great Healing Power, to Perfect Faith,
out of the damp circle of her
bladder's yellow tickle and betrayal.

TASTING A NEW MOON

Robert Miltner

"*The croissant is dignified, born of tender care and craftsmanship. Bakers carefully layer the dough, paint on perfect proportions of butter, and then roll and fold this trembling croissant embryo with the precision of a Japanese origami master.*"

—Association of French Bakers, in
response to Kanye West's criticism of
croissants in one of his songs

My mother's idea of baking involved opening a package of bake-at-home dough. A child of the Depression, she had grown up on Cleveland's near West Side eating home-baked loaves of white bread made from bleached flour. After WWII, she was captivated by the new time-saving and always-available store-bought packages of sliced bread. As much as my two brothers and I couldn't get enough of our Grandma Ethel's fresh home-baked bread, hand-sliced while still oven warm, we were keen to the ease of grabbing slices of

Wonder Bread from the bread box, slathering them with Skippy or Jif peanut butter and Welch's Concord grape jelly, then running out the door for a game of pick-up baseball or to explore the woods and fields at the end of our street in Northeast Ohio.

Ease became my mother's culinary motto, evident over the years as she replaced the Christmas tradition of making her own cookies from scratch; instead, she drove her little blue Ford Falcon to the nearby Sparkle Supermarket to buy knock-out gingerbread men and assembly-line iced cut-outs. Following suit, she dedicated herself to baking biscuits from prepackaged dough. Not only was it quick and easy, but the scent of just-from-the-oven pastry wafted from the small kitchen stove through the rest of our suburban ranch house. Her motherly duties were complete when she set the cloth towel-lined bowl of finished "fresh" baked biscuits on the dinner table. It was at such a dinner that I encountered my first croissant.

––––––––

But it wasn't an *actual* croissant. My mother had just popped open a thin cylinder constructed of cardboard with tin end caps that held packaged biscuit dough. After extruding the separated circular disks, she arranged the dough discs in rows on a cookie tray, rolled and reshaped them into something resembling a bell curve, then stretched the ends into points, sort of like a gooey white smile. She called them crescent rolls.

What I knew of crescents I'd discovered in the *Encyclopedia Britannica* that my parents had purchased for my two brothers and me. In the volume that included the letter *E* for Egypt, I first read about the Fertile Crescent, which included the Euphrates, Tigris, and the Nile rivers—synonymous with the Cradle of Civilization comprised of Upper and Lower Egypt, Mesopotamia,

Assyria, Phoenicia, and Palestine. On the map, it resembled a quarter moon, either waxing or waning. On the table where we ate supper, the towel-lined bowl held warm crescent dinner rolls.

––––––––

But not just *any* dinner rolls. These were crescent rolls produced by the Pillsbury Company; the company had come to national prominence in 1949 when it began hosting the National Bake-off at the Waldorf Astoria Hotel in New York City. A year later, they introduced, in the new supermarkets of the 1950s, packaged dough offered in the "Give it a pop!" cylinders. In what today would look like an episode of *Mad Men*, Rudy Perz, copywriter for Pillsbury's ad agency, imagined the wad of dough morphing into a small, pudgy doll that came to life. Pillsbury had found its mascot, the Doughboy, who was soon accompanied by a catchy sing-along jingle that celebrated, in an edited slant rhyme, how mothers could take "lovin'" from the "oven" and serve their families ready-made emotions every bit as warm as grandma's home-baked bread.

When my parents went out with their friends for dinner and drinks, my mother would leave my brothers and me with a special treat: crescent dogs, with the dough wrapped around an Oscar Meyer wiener and a folded slice of Kraft American cheese, always best served with a side of tater tots. Such culinary artistry was a clear indication that regional cuisine was changing in the Midwest during the early 1960s. Why waste time on local apple cider, fresh cake donuts, or clam bakes in the autumn when all you needed to do was whistle for the crescent dogs to come running?

As the use of refrigerated pastry grew, so too did its shelf life, from weeks to months. Concurrent with such product development was the rise of margarine products—vegetable oils joined by beta carotene for yellow coloring and isolated natural butter compounds for a "real" imitation butter flavor—that, when added to refrigerated pastry, did not go rancid. Along this trajectory, Pillsbury went beyond the successful crescent roll, adding the new Butter Flake line that made the crescent roll more like its French cousin, that is, an *actual* croissant. But I was young then, eating those crescent dogs, and I did not know that what I took as real was merely a simulacra, a false version of the actual.

———

My early childhood was spent along the Rocky River in Cleveland's "Emerald Necklace" Metroparks—a natural world of newts and under-rock salamanders, birds' nests, and long-as-my-legs gar swimming leisurely against the slow current of the river. Then my parents moved to Cleveland's western suburbs near Avon Point along the north coast of Lake Erie. My great-grandfather Patrick Higgins had earned his living on Lake Erie as a pleasure boat captain, leaving from Cleveland's East Ninth Street pier and going west to Detroit and east to Buffalo. My own childhood hours spent fishing from the concrete piers behind the electric power plant were a miniscule substitute for my great-grandfather's Great Lakes life.

For some impulse impossible to articulate beyond my late adolescent understanding, I attended my first year of college in Steubenville, the first actual city in which I lived. In retrospect, I now see that I sought something more "real" than the semi-rural expanding suburban I had experienced up until that time. The hilltop location of the college campus gave me a wide view of the old industrial city built along the slow-moving Ohio River, one far larger than the knee-deep-in-places Rocky River of my early childhood. This grand river was different, for it seemed to hold some vague truths awaiting my discovery.

My sophomore year I transferred downriver to attended Xavier University, a Jesuit institution in Cincinnati, the largest city I'd lived in up to that time. From up in Eden Park, I could see the great swath of river below me. One day when I was feeling curious, I discovered an old set of leaning concrete steps I could walk down all the way to the near-downtown banks of the Ohio River. I marveled at the heady feeling of experiencing something so large and powerful, comparable to what I'd seen before only in books or an encyclopedia. In that moment, I encountered an *actual* river. Looking upriver, I could see the future coming toward my 19-year-old self, see it momentarily flow slowly in front of me, and watch it, like my past, as it curved with the landscape and receded.

I spent a lot of time off campus that year, actually. I was either down in Clifton, a bohemian district near the University of Cincinnati, or up in Mount Adams, an old German neighborhood that was experiencing early gentrification by capitalistic hippies and college stoners. I discovered a coffee shop that made espresso in small aluminum Bialetti makers, a method startlingly different from the instant coffee my parents constantly drank. Rich and strong as the imported chocolate I was discovering, complex and lush as the French wines I was trying, espresso was as compact and dense as the hashish my peers were smoking. My impressionable 19-year-old taste buds were so in love that I spent starstruck hours peering into the demitasse of espresso as if into the eye of a new lover. Once, though, my infatuation was interrupted when a perky barista asked me if I wanted anything to eat along with my espresso.

"Let me get you a croissant," she said.

———

It was love at first sight. The creamy, almost new-snow color. The lightly browned tips and the top layer baked to crisp perfection. I pulled lightly from each horned end as if it were a pastry party favor. The croissant practically unraveled into two pieces in my hands, the lacy white interior delicate as a tatted doily, that decorative *frivolité* set on a china plate upon which sweet pastries are placed and presented. O, the breathtaking near-weightlessness. O, the scent of—wait—real butter. And the taste was love at first bite: buttered air, sweet dough, enough luscious gluten to send me into a carb coma.

This was the cotton candy of the pastry world. This was the crescent waxing toward the full-moon dream cuisine of the gourmand, *bon vivant*, epicurean, and hedonist. There, right there at my small table next to my notebook, sat the espresso and a croissant. But it was more than mere love: it was complete abandonment to my newfound bliss. From then on, I would always get a table for three. *Bon appétit!*

———

According to Prosper Montagné, author of the 1938 *Larousse Gastromonique: The Encyclopedia of Food, Wine & Cookery* (American translation, 1961, third printing), one finds among the roughly 8,500 recipes scattered over its 1,100 pages, the alphabetical index for croissants on pages 322–323. Since the coeditor of the 1938 first edition, Philéas Gilbert, calls the volume "a reliable counsellor ready to be consulted," I accept the origin story of the croissant as presented by Montagné to be true. He dates it to the 1686 siege of Budapest by the Turks. Bakers busy at night making breads discerned the sound of the tunneling Turks and gave alarm, saving the city. To honor their heroic act, the bakers were rewarded with permission to create a special pastry that resembled the crescent moon emblem from the Ottoman flag. Oddly, Montagné does not narrate how this Hungarian delight traveled to become the distinct pastry of the *boulangeries* and *pâtisseries* of France. I'll assume word of mouth.

———

When I visited in Paris in 2008, I made it my mission to taste as many actual French croissants as possible, both early in the morning at the Montparnasse brasseries with espresso or in the well-lighted late-night brasseries joined by Médoc and Bordeaux wines. I proclaimed each croissant a tie with those previously sampled and ordered more. Paris, in my mind, was home to the absolute and ultimate croissant experience, comparable to a trip to Mecca or Wrigley Field. But then in 2014, my wife, Molly, and I went to Old Québec City, Canada, described in my *Lonely Planet* guidebook as the next best thing to a European walled city, and very French at that.

———

The Château des Tourelles is an 1898 turreted three-story house turned into a bed-and-breakfast. It is conveniently located a leisurely 15-minute walk down Rue Saint-Jean toward the Porte Saint-Jean entrance in the castle-like walls of Old Québec. The turret of the château comprises five stories and a narrow hallway leading to the flat roof where guests find a wooden deck with iron railings. The deck offers a panoramic view of Église Saint-Jean-Baptiste, the city streets, the huge St. Lawrence River, and the low blue mountains that lie north of the city. Our second night on the roof, we finished a bottle of lush Two Sisters Niagara Cabernet Franc and opened a local cuvée from the Ste-Pétronille Vineyards on Ile d'Orléans. The next morning, we decided to have lunch on the rooftop, so we set out to purchase some local goat cheese plus a baguette or croissant to have with the rest of the cuvée.

When asked for shopping recommendations, William, the young French-Canadian manager of the château, said that almost every block in the Old City had a cheese shop, but there was really only one place to buy croissants: Le Pain Grüel, an artisanal bakery on Rue Saint-Jean known for its organic ancient grain breads. When we asked him for the address, William laughed and told us to follow our noses.

———

Le Pain Grüel (or Au Pain Grüel or Boulangerie Paingrüel or Le Paingrüel Boulangerie de Créative) is located at 578 Rue Saint-Jean. Walking down the sidewalk toward Québec's Old City walls, I wondered whether the bakery actually existed or not, or if it had been lost in translation; perhaps it was some sort of French-Canadian *boulangerie* mirage.

Then at the same moment, Molly and I stopped on the sidewalk. We stood absolutely still. We raised out heads, sniffing the air like scent hounds ready for a chase.

An intense fresh-baked bread scent intoxicated us, enchanted us, drew us up the concrete steps; we walked like puppets through the spring-green door and into Le Pain Grüel bakery.

Warm oak cabinets, earth-colored tile floors and counters, and rich red trim: they felt perfect for this *boulangerie*. We sampled small bites of day-old rye bread and stood transfixed as soldiers at attention in front of baskets of baguettes standing like swords raised against the mediocrity of commercial baking. Then I turned and saw the cooling rack, laden like a treasure chest with spilled golden crescent coins.

I stared like a man entranced. I wasn't breathing. I actually couldn't talk.

Instead, I could only point and did.

"How many croissants?" the baker asked. "Two," I croaked. "No, three."

"Make it four," Molly added.

———

After picking up a round of local goat brie and crisp green apples from a small grocery on Rue Saint-Jean, we walked back up to the Château des Tourelles, our strides as long as baguettes, our hearts rising like new loaves, our hands entwined like braided bread dough.

Though the sun on the rooftop deck was warm, a cool late May breeze touched our necks. I looked up from the St. Lawrence River, as magical as the Ohio River had seemed when I was younger. I turned my focus to the sky, seeking a leftover sliver of moon, but there was none. My wife and I chewed half-slices of apple, each of us lulling in a gluten buzz.

My crescent roll journey was ending, my archetypal narrative coming to its final point of arrival, like an errant knight's quest completed. The buttery piece of light dough I'd removed from the center of the croissant with my left hand was soft and pliant like just-steamed mussels nesting in a warm ceramic bowl, or like the soft wax tears from poppies used to make opium. I was hooked.

SHARKS

Kenneth Parson

"The worm has turned," J. D. says and sinks the nine ball, stopping the cue ball dead on the spot where white and yellow clacked, for his first money ball in nearly an hour. Charlie, Rabbit, and Woody go to the table and each lays two one-dollar bills next to the front left corner pocket, the pay-off spot when a money ball goes down. J. D. reaches over and picks up the six bills, stuffs them in his shirt pocket, sucks air through the stem of his unlit pipe, and chalks his cue stick, mulling in his mind over the balls that Rabbit is racking up.

I could have gone out shotgunning beers with my buddies on LeMaster Hill, smoking weed with long-haired, fried Larry for the first time in my near-18 years on this earth or fishing all night on the Ohio River near the C&O roundhouse. But I'd rather be here. Squatting on a pop crate at Darby's Grocery and Game Room, 1:15 a.m. Sunday morning, watching the sharks.

"What do you say we make it five on the three and six, ten on the nine, and call it quits at two?" Woody asks, the first time he's spouted out more than three words all night.

"Fine with me," J. D. says through his teeth that clench his pipe.

"I can stand it," Charlie says, kind of direct but polite, and he pulls a pouch of Red Horse from his jeans' pocket.

"Bust 'em," Charlie's younger brother Rabbit says, motioning towards the table with his stick, glaring trancelike and just plain-ass losing.

J. D.'s break cracks like a 22 bullet—a lot of scattering colors and noisy motion, but nothing's falling. The last ball moving slaps rapidly back and forth on the rubber of the right side pocket; then stops, as still as an egg, barely a hair's breadth from dropping in.

"Robbed," J. D. says, swinging his elbow and pool stick up towards the ceiling, following through with the shot, as if his momentum and his body English would make the two ball fall.

"The table robbed you, huh, J. D.?" Woody jokes and strikes a kitchen match against the cinderblock wall to fire up his Pall Mall.

J. D. has been smarting off at Woody all night, ever since they started playing around nine thirty. And seeing how J. D. owns both pool tables, the juke box, and the pinball machines in the game room, I reckon Woody is starting to dish out a little payback, hinting that there might be a slight defect in the pool table itself.

Charlie springs to the table and stoops to better eyeball the position of the one, but I can tell from where I'm sitting, he ain't got much of a shot. He bobs his head up and down and from side to side, but the one is hidden by three other balls at the upper end of the table. Long green.

"Stymied," Charlie mumbles to himself.

He stops chewing on his wad of Red Horse, crouches into position, and kicks the cue ball hard off the right rail and it gets a piece of the one; three or four balls slap and tap, but nothing falls. Pacing from the table, his eyes glare right at the one ball like it's one evil SOB, and his jaw steadily works his chewing tobacco. He picks up a pop can from the cement floor and pulls out his Case Double X Hawkbill to make a spittoon, on account he knows it could be a good while before he gets to shoot again.

Squinting from the smoke of the Pall Mall unfiltered stringing from his lips, Woody's eyes dance over the balls, his face heavy with that same sad, worried expression he's had since the first day he came slouch-assed into the pool room four or five weeks ago, saying he was from California and had come to Kentucky to visit his uncle, and asking if he could get a game. Damn those droopy eyes and large floppy, fin-like ears. When I first saw him, I wondered how flesh and bone could hold up such a weighed-down, wearisome-looking soul.

J. D. taps his stick ever so lightly on the floor, maybe to annoy Woody, or perhaps to get him to hurry up, or to break his rhythm, seeing how Woody's kinda the nervous type.

Woody jerks his neck to flick back a stray lock of dark brown hair from his eyes, but it falls right back again, so he brushes it back with two fingers, only to have it come back in his eyes again. He pays no more attention to it, as if he's looking right through it, or as if it were no longer there, no longer an aggravation. Finally, he drops his Pall Mall to the floor, crushes it under the sole of his over-sized Red Ball Jets white high-tops, and lowers his long torso over the table, with his chin less than a foot from the green felt and his pool stick cocked high in his left hand. He pumps the stick sharp and quick, and the cue ball snaps the one and clears the four by a hair and drops dead center

169

in the left side pocket with a loud thud. He raises up, takes three steps, gets right back into position and buries the two, running the cue ball off two rails to the other end of the table for perfect shape on the three. In a lightning-white clap, he buries the three in the corner and the cue ball spirals off at a right angle and taps the six resting two inches from the opposite corner pocket. The six takes the two ball's kiss, then rolls and drops into the pocket.

J. D. pulls his pipe from his mouth and howls out, "Mercy . . . two money balls in one shot?"

Charlie arches his eyebrows in disbelief, holding his pop can suspended a few inches below his lip.

Rabbit blinks his eyes rapidly three times, and then slides deeper into his loser's trance.

"The worm *has* turned, J. D.," Woody calls out, without taking his eyes from the table. He returns to his shooter's stance, chalks his stick's tip and runs the remaining five balls in quick succession: aim, fire; aim, fire; aim, fire, using low English on the cue ball on every shot. When the nine ball falls, he walks away from the table without showing any sign of victory on his face and goes right back to his spot where he slouches against the wall when he ain't shootin, a few feet from where I'm sitting. He watches as the other players put their money on the table near the left corner pocket—thirty bucks each, and walks over, picks up the bills and then comes back in his slow, shambling pace.

"You want a bottle of pop?" he asks me.

"Yeah, sure," I say, surprised that he even acknowledges I'm in the room.

"Go get us one, and a bag of chips apiece, too," he says.

He folds the bills and puts 'em into his pants' front pocket, all except for one, a five-spot that jitters between his index and third fingers as he holds it out to me.

I take the five and rush out of the game room, past Wanda, who's working late tonight, sitting behind the counter and collecting a nickel a game from each player for a rack fee. The grocery store closes every night at 10, but sometimes they stay open late when J. D.'s got a game up. Wanda's been watching from the two-by-three-foot hole that lets the person behind the counter watch what's going on at the pool tables, juke box, and pinball machines.

I pull two bottles of Barq's root beer from the pop cooler. It's Woody's brand. I know; I've seen him sipping it before. As I open the second bottle, Woody's break explodes so loud I swear it rattles the plywood partition that separates the pop case area from the game room. I grab two bags of Tom's chips from the stand next to the cooler and hurry to the counter to give Wanda the five.

"I ain't never seen shootin' like that," she says, her eyes wide open like she's seen a ghost or something.

For the next 40 minutes, it's mostly Woody shooting, and J. D., Charlie, Rabbit, me and Wanda watching. J. D. and Charlie are barely able to muster a money ball each, but Rabbit can't muster a damn thing. It ain't that Rabbit is such a bad shot; it's just that during those few times that Woody don't make a ball, he leaves Rabbit sewed up to where he can't even get a good hit on the ball, let alone get a halfway decent shot.

At 2:02 a.m., Woody buries the nine and J. D., Charlie, and Rabbit lean their sticks against the wall and lay down their five- and ten-dollar bills. J. D. and Rabbit walk away without saying a word—J. D. sucking air through his unlit pipe, and Rabbit staring straight ahead, probably regretting he ever picked up a pool stick.

"Good shootin', Woody," Charlie says, breaking the silence, and smiles sort of gentlemanly like, then he turns his head. "Hey, Wanda, need a ride home?" He's gonna come out winning something tonight, one way or another.

Everybody who comes into the game room has always figured there's been something going on between Charlie and Wanda, although he's married with a couple of kids and all. I know I heard Rabbit ask Charlie earlier if he wasn't supposed to be pulling the hoot owl shift at the steel mill, but Charlie said he "called off." I get up off the pop crate and all this makes me sorta laugh to myself, all kinda comical-like.

"You walkin up the road?" Woody asks me, really catching me off guard.

"Yeah, sure," I answer, wondering why he asked me, but I guess we are kinda like neighbors.

We go out the door and Wanda's right behind us to lock up, with her keys jingling, and Charlie at close range staring at her bottom. J. D. pulls out of the lot in his Ford truck, the German shepherd that's always inside on the passenger's side has its ears perked up and tongue hanging, no doubt woke up from a long snooze, and no doubt glad to be headed home. Rabbit leaves in his shiny candy-apple red Toronado in a soft peel-out, slinging a light spray of gravel behind the car's dual-extended tailpipes.

Me and Woody walk down the main road of Mossy Bottom, the white, single-story houses and brown-shingled half-shacks still and quiet, the lights long turned off. The early September night air makes it all seem kind of sweet and peaceful, and I sort of feel like I'm the big winner of the night, for some unknown reason.

"You sure was shootin' good tonight. How much you win?" I ask.

"Three-fifty, maybe four hundred," Woody answers blunt-like.

"I hope I can shoot pool as good as you one day," I say, but I get no reply. "Why do you use low English all the time?" I ask, trying to show him I know a little something about shooting pool.

"How old are you?" Woody asks, twitching his shoulder in my direction, but he don't look at me.

"Seventeen," I answer.

He pulls out a Pall Mall from his shirt pocket and a Zippo lighter from his tan khaki pants, and I'm thinking, Why the hell does he always use kitchen matches to light his smoke when he's shooting pool when he's got a lighter? I start to ask him for a cigarette, but I figure I'd better not, 'cause I really don't want to bother him too much.

"You still in school?" Woody asks and lights his Pall Mall.

"I graduated this year, class of '71," I answer, trying to raise a bit of pride in my voice, as most students 'round my age don't graduate till they're 18.

"What ya goin' to do now?" he asks.

"Ain't sure," I answer, tired of hearing this question that's been put to me by everybody from my great aunt in St. Petersburg, Florida, to Wanda at Darby's.

"Pool is just a game," he says, and still he don't look at me. "It's not nothin' for you to care 'bout."

I hold my tongue for a while, but finally I get up my spunk to speak.

"If it's just a game, then why are you so serious all the time, Woody?" I finally blurt out.

Woody lets out a quick breath of air, a kind of huffing sound, and his lower lip curls up a little—the first time I've ever seen him respond to anything with what could be made out to be a kind of laugh; yet he still doesn't say a word. So I let it go, and we walk on in silence.

When we come to the railroad tracks that divide county property from city property, that separate Mossy Bottom from Hollowell, and my path home from Woody's walk down the road to his uncle's, I ask him, "You gonna be shootin' tomorrow night?"

"Nah. I'm takin the bus back to California 'bout nine tomorrow night," he answers.

"Okay. Woody, it was good meetin' you and watchin' you shoot pool. See you when you come back around," I say, as I wave a hand and walk straight ahead, pretending that what he said ain't no big surprise.

"You, too," he replies, and he turns right on the street just past the railroad tracks.

I cross the street but don't head up the hill toward home. I stop under the streetlight and watch Woody walking down the road, kinda like he's swimming off in the darkness. He twitches his neck occasionally, still trying to get the hair out of his eyes, and a thin stream of smoke trails over his left shoulder. I watch him walk on until all I see is a blue-on-white plaid shirt and baggy, tan khaki pants, until he finally he disappears down a dip in the road.

At that moment, I know that whatever Woody has that makes him a damn good pool player, a pool shark—and I ain't got a clue as to what that is—no, I don't think I'll ever have it. And thinking about this makes me think about myself, and what's next for me, like Woody asked, and I really don't know. But I know one thing's for sure: I won't be around a pool table tomorrow if Woody's not there.

And I can't stop thinking about Woody, about who and what he is, besides a pool shark, and where he's going, and where he's been; but then again, I don't know if any of that even matters. I look into the darkness that he walked into, and I really, really wonder if there was some part of Woody that was ever here at all. Some part of him that he lost or left somewhere in some other little river town, maybe in some other kind of game, a long, long time ago.

GIRL MEETS CAR

Laura Power

I used to be the kind of girl who owned a sports car. I know this because I have a picture of me sitting on the first car I ever bought, a damask-red convertible MG Midget with a black vinyl top and interior. My mother, who feared and hated cars, and didn't even know how to drive, snapped the photo in 1977. She could not fathom that she had raised a sports-car-owning daughter. Was this the girl, the dutiful daughter, who in her teen years had dried the dishes every night; who cried on the single occasion she handed in homework late; who wore her hemlines at the knee in the mini-skirt era; who kowtowed to every curfew, rule, and demand her parents could devise? The photograph was an essential commemoration to the unbelievability of it all.

My Midget was a small car, only 141 inches long and 54 inches wide, just big enough for the two passenger seats wedged inside. When I stood by it, the top of the roof barely reached my waist, but when I sat inside, I felt like it had been built around me. Driving down the highway, I was encased in a speeding bullet, my legs stretched down into the well that held the brake, the clutch, and the gas pedals, my right hand resting lightly on the stick shift, my head tilting back just a little against the seat. I raced, zipped, screamed by debris I wished to spin off: my harshly lit, under-furnished apartment, the sweaty, self-absorbed boys who asked me on dates, the bank that housed my almost perpetually empty checking account.

I got the idea to buy an MG Midget from my college-days boyfriend, the hobbit-like Bill, with his bowl haircut and paunch pushing on his belt even at 21.

But Bill could be fun; he was smart, and, at least in a car, he was patient. He taught me to drive his manual shift MG Midget on the hilly, heavily trafficked streets of Pittsburgh. My own father could not tolerate my driving; he sent me at age 16 to driver education class after one short spin in a deserted parking lot. Bill, though, stuck with me lesson after lesson.

Our routine went like this: Hunch down into car. No seatbelts, we wouldn't wear them anyway. Put right foot on the brake, left on clutch. Hold breath, bite lower lip, turn key. Jiggle stick shift, okay, in neutral. Take foot off brake. Hit gas. Feel rpms shoot up. Scream. Calm down, engage first gear. Barely make out Bill's voice, coming from somewhere. "Now let the clutch out slowly and give it just a little gas." Gasp for breath, can't get one. Take foot off brake, tap gas. Rpms shoot up. Barely, lightly press gas. Millimeter by millimeter let out clutch. Panic. Hit gas. Grit teeth at the whine of gear hitting gear. "Grind me a pound while you're at it. Ha-ha." Lurch forward. Stomp brake. Jerk to stop. Stall engine. Hear Bill laugh like hyena. Resolve to try again.

We went through this routine more times than I can count. After weeks of sweating, grinding, crying practice, I finally learned to drive the Midget. I got so good, so smooth at shifting gears that unless you saw me move the stick shift, you wouldn't know when I shifted from first to second or second to third. It became a game to me to watch the tachometer and know exactly the right moment to shift. I liked especially to drift in towards a red light, never completely coming to a stop. And then, just when the light turned green, hit the gas pedal and zip through the intersection. It was cool then, particularly for a girl, to know how to drive a manual shift car.

Bill and I went everywhere in that car, and often, I did the driving. I zipped around trucks, sneaking up from behind and blasting past, been and gone before they could even honk. It was dangerous, but I didn't think about that. And Bill, he wasn't compulsive or greedy about his car. We'd ride with the top down and eat chocolate ice cream cones dipped in cherry coating, even on hot days. He cleaned up the drips afterward. Once we drove the Midget 24 hours straight, to Florida. Bill, the Midget, and I camped out at Disney World. We cruised in Fort Lauderdale. We drove right down the beach in Daytona.

The end began for Bill and me when he graduated from college and moved to Cleveland. Our long-distance relationship was tempestuous. One day he'd call to say he loved me, and cry that he couldn't possibly be without me. Would I transfer schools and move to Cleveland? But then, I might not hear from him for two or three weeks. He'd sound surprised if I phoned him, he was busy with work, what was the problem? When he did come to visit in his red MG Midget, we had fun, but more and more often, his brooding dampened our weekends. We broke up a few times, but I couldn't make it stick. I kept telling myself it was Bill I couldn't be without. But maybe it was his car; maybe that's what bound us long after I was worn down from emotional yo-yoing.

We eventually said our final goodbye in the Midget. As my graduation approached, my parents, who lived nearby, planned a celebration. Bill drove down. We spent the evening and morning before the party in impatient near-silence. I had resolved, almost completely decided, that, car or no car, love was finished; it was time to give it up. I planned to wait until after the party to talk, but after driving the first few blocks toward home, I pulled into a parking lot and killed the ignition. I rested my forehead on the steering wheel, and we looked at each other. He ran his finger under the crisscross strap of my red sundress.

"Okay," he said, "I know we're done." I slid out of the car.

The Midget's black vinyl top was splotched with the rain that had just begun to fall, but I patted it with more affection than I'd afforded Bill. Back at the dorm, I called my Dad to pick me up.

"Bill's car broke down," I said.

I bought my own MG Midget a few months later. I was working at my first real job, and before long I had saved enough money for a down payment. I never considered any other car. There was only one MG dealer near where I worked, and I marched right over there and ordered up the red Midget. No discussion. No negotiation.

I was the only person I knew then with an MG Midget, and I liked that. When I drove it to work for the first time, all the guys from the traffic and shipping departments came out at lunch to look it over. Those who could fit sat in it. Several glanced at me sidelong and asked, "Can you really drive that thing?" They all seemed to be impressed.

The Midget was finicky, but I did not mind. It often refused to start when it was wet from rain or snow, but I got good at starting it by popping the clutch while coasting downhill.

It was a novelty, that car, for a girl like me who was raised on Chevrolet

Impalas. The Midget created a sense of fun wherever I took it. I drove it around with the top down, eating french fries, and napped in it with the sun in my face. Bill faded to a distant memory, and I got a new boyfriend. He and I flew the Midget around town; we ferried between his house and my apartment, top down, hair flying, clothes beating with the wind. When we went out, we almost always left his old Audi Fox parked and lonely in the driveway.

When I took my Midget to my parents' home for the first time, everyone wanted to drive it except my mother. Even my dad wanted to take it for a spin, although at six foot one, he could barely fit in it. When he pulled back into the driveway after a short tour, the Midget would not let him get out. He opened the little side door and tried to pull his legs up out of the well under the steering wheel, but he couldn't bend his knees deeply enough to escape. When grunting and pulling on his knees didn't work, he had to put his hands down on the gravelly driveway and fall out.

My Midget and I were an item for two years, until I quit work to go to graduate school. I noodled and scribbled, I phoned, and I calculated, but I couldn't devise a way to pay the tuition without selling that car. I made one last, long drive in it, back to Pittsburgh. After eight hours of shifting, coasting, running up those rpms, my baby rolled to a stop in my parents' driveway. That's where I last saw it. My dad sold it for me. At about that same time, the British Leland Company, who made the Midget, stopped manufacturing it. I never had another car like it.

When I next had money for a car, I bought a huge old Chevrolet nicknamed "the big green booger." It got me around, but I dangled the photo of me and my Midget from the booger's rearview mirror.

OLD BLUE VOLVO

Mike Schneider

Twenty horses and a crank starter—
  never made 'em better
    than the Tin Lizzie
said Grandpa, a machinist
          at the brass mill,
the Model T a shining image,
          youth and freedom.
Henry Ford—two words jangling
in his pocket: Living wage.
      Eight-hour day.

Dad loved the '48 half-ton
    he found for a few bucks,
gave it fresh plugs, a bumper, played
  with the timing till it hummed.
Loved me too,
    though he couldn't say it.
With that rattly pickup showed me
    manual transmission,
      hands-on, sequenced
pattern of the letter H, metallic
      industrial click

of shifted gears. Quietly
    he'd shake his head
as that old truck bucked
     & quivered to a dead stop.
Feel the free play in the pedal.
    Let it out slow, then give it gas.

Soon, I was double-clutching
    on the downshift,
taking raw joy
    in the engine's roar
& surge, pulling deep
    into the furnace of itself
to charge uphill
    like a young man
propelling himself into the world.

Now it's my daughter, sixteen,
        at the wheel.
Our old blue Volvo jumps.
    The dashboard lights up red.
She groans. Quietly
    I shake my head—
this strange voice
    on my tongue.
Let it up till it grabs, then feather it.
    Easy. That's the way.

BAGEL MACHER

E. G. Silverman

Fat, sweaty, and bald except for a few greasy strands of hair that he was forever combing back with his pudgy baker's hands, Herman Goldman gave all new employees of Bagel Macher a stern lecture on the rules of his shop.

"Don't drop the bagels, Feldstein," he warned me, emphatically pronouncing each word slowly, separately, to make sure I understood. "To you, they're a bagel. To me, they're eight cents."

In 1970, a bagel cost eight cents.

"Always stir the *mehal kehal* this way," he proclaimed, demonstrating the proper technique. His *t*'s sounded like *h*'s with his accent, which he had brought with him from Brooklyn to open Squirrel Hill's first bagel shop, the first anywhere in Pittsburgh.

"And never accept any collect calls! Never! I don't care if it's the president. I don't care if it's the pope. I don't care if it's Jesus Christ himself. No collect calls!"

Herman was peering right past me at Maria Debonna, and he delivered his decree loud enough to make sure she heard it. Herman assumed that all non-Jews were Catholics, and he believed in the necessity of invoking Jesus, the pope, or both, whenever lecturing the goyim on weighty matters.

Herman thrust out his chin and grunted. His scowl dared her to refute him.

"What if it's your wife?" Maria shot back, her voice clear and hard.

Herman charged past me, past the stainless-steel trough into which the bagels were dumped after they were boiled and before they were laid out in fours on wooden boards to go into the oven, past the baskets that held the bagels after they came out of the oven, and up to where Maria stood behind the customer counter, beside the cash register.

Maria had lustrous black hair in a wonderful confusion of curls, waves, and flips. Her white blouse was unbuttoned to the top of her Bagel Macher apron, and I could see a shiny gold heart on her chest. She chewed gum, had little lines for eyebrows over brown eyes and lashes heavy with mascara, and she wore white lipstick that glistened like vanilla frosting.

She handed a customer a paper bag full of bagels with two plastic bags to put them in once they cooled, took the money, made change, and ended the transaction with a polite thank-you. The woman smiled pleasantly and wished Maria a good day.

"Smart mouth," Herman declared as soon as the customer was gone. "I hope you're not smart-talking the customers."

"Fine. Your wife calls collect, I'll tell the operator her husband says to go fuck herself."

The front door opened, tinkling the bell over it, and a woman in tennis whites strolled up to the counter.

Herman loomed over Maria, his two hundred pounds against her one hundred, his stubby finger stabbing at the air so close to her nose that a white speck of flour landed on her cheek.

"I hear that word out of your trashy mouth again and you're fired."

She peeled off her apron, squashed it into a ball, and stuffed it into his gut so hard that he gasped.

"You take this fucking job and stick it up your ass," she snapped. She opened a drawer, grabbed her purse, slammed the drawer, and stormed out, leaving Herman standing there huffing, her apron in his hands.

"You can't do that!" he shouted. "Maria, you get back in here right now or you're fired."

The woman in whites waited to place her order, pretending she didn't hear.

I was being hired only for the summer and would be making the bagels, not answering the phone, so I was as peripheral to this conversation as the gleaming stainless-steel kettle that bubbled away like a witch's caldron. Now, with Maria gone, Herman remembered me, still standing by the kettle.

"You, Feldstein, get over here," he snarled. "I should pay you to keep the floor from flying away?"

As I approached him, Herman noticed the apron in his hands and threw it at me with disgust.

"And what am I supposed to do on a Friday, busiest day of the week and nobody to wait on customers?" he panted, his hands palms up to the heavens.

"I could learn to run the register," I suggested.

His glower told me I might as well have proposed that he open a store on the moon.

"Macher! Boys make the bagels. Pretty girls sell the bagels."

Then to the lady in whites, "May I help you?"

"Half dozen water, quarter dozen pumpernickel, quarter poppy, and half dozen bialys," she said. "And make sure they're fresh."

"All our bagels are right out of the oven. What kind do you want for your free one?"

"Raisin."

"Raisin. Right. Here you go. A dollar forty-four."

She hunted for pennies in the bottom of her purse. I thought Herman was going to snatch it from her and get them himself.

"Thank you and have a nice day," he offered with a slight bow as he handed her the bags. "And be careful you shouldn't burn yourself. They're still hot."

The woman clutched the paper bags, scrutinized the contents, and counted. She frowned, counted again, decided they were all there, mumbled a good-bye, and left.

Herman watched the door shut behind her and grumbled, "Go ahead, count them. I should cheat you? I ever cheated anybody? Go eat your raisin bagel."

Then it was my turn.

"You, Joel. You go get Maria. Probably down at Giovanni's stuffing her face with pizza so she'll get zits. Go bring her back."

"But . . . I . . . What do I say? . . . How do I . . .?"

"Don't argue. Do it already."

The door opened and a pair of elderly ladies bustled in, their silver hair coifed as if they'd just been to the beauty parlor together. Herman greeted them and our conversation was over.

The pizza shop was a block and a half down Murray Avenue, past one of

Squirrel Hill's two remaining kosher butchers with its sawdust-covered floor, live chickens in crates out on the sidewalk.

Maria was sitting in a corner booth, filing her nails.

I stood before her, intrigued, intimidated, but not nervous. I sensed something gentle in her, something disarming.

"Herman sent you?" she said, holding her hand at arm's length, fingers splayed so she could inspect them.

"Uh huh."

"Sit down. You're making me nervous."

I slid into the booth opposite her and tried not to stare.

"You like my nails?" she said. "I think I have ugly hands. Not surprising working them to the bone in that damned bakery."

I had never thought of it as a bakery. To me a bakery and a bagel shop were two entirely different things. It would have been like calling a tennis court a gymnasium.

"What do you want to work there for anyway?" she said.

"I don't know. It's a job."

"Give me your hands."

I laid my hands on the table. She took one, held it in hers, turned it over, and traced her finger over the lines of my palm.

"Now the other one."

She did the same thing to my other hand.

"You have nice hands," she said. "Long life lines."

She ran a finger up my wrist and along my forearm and the inside of my elbow and then down again. Her touch was light, sure, sensual, and suggestive.

I'd had girlfriends and held hands and done a lot more than that, but this was different. Maria was older, probably 20 or more, from Greenfield, and not Jewish. She was an adult, knew about things I did not, and in her finger was an invitation to share experiences I had only dreamed of. I felt myself bulging in my pants.

"This is just a summer job for you, isn't it?" she said softly, her brown eyes gazing into mine. "Then you go off to college and become a doctor or lawyer or something?"

"I have another year," I admitted meekly.

She left my hands sitting on the table next to the sugar dispenser and picked up her coffee.

"I wanted to be a manicurist," she mused, holding the cup to her chin. "Or a beautician. Maybe own my own shop one day."

She had little gold hearts for earrings. They bobbed when she talked.

"Why don't you?"

She put the cup down and smiled patiently at me.

"What's your father do?" she asked.

"He's a dentist."

"Mine worked in the mills. Now he's sick and sits around all day. He can hardly breathe. My mother works at the mills, too, but she's in the office, so it's not so bad. She wanted to get me a job there, but I said no thank you."

I was staring now. Right at her face, her mouth, her cheeks, her eyes, her chest with the open buttons and the heart pendant. She was staring right back at me, so it was okay.

"At least I got to finish school, you know? But I'm not like you. No daddy to pay for college. I'm not playing summer job at the bakery. This is my life. This is all I have. You understand?"

She wasn't telling me this to hold it over me, the way a lot of people would have—the "I'm better than you 'cause I'm worse off than you" speech. No, she was telling me so I would understand her. So I would know her. And there was nothing I wanted more at that moment than to know everything about her. I would have told her anything about me.

I wanted her to touch me again, to run her finger over my hand, across my wrist, up the inside of my arm.

"So Joel. What did Herman tell you to tell me?"

"He wants you to come back."

"That's it?"

"I think he really does. He needs you to come back. He needs you to wait on the customers."

"The dumb fuck. You know, he really grates on my nerves, the fat pig."

I wanted to touch her hair. The girls I knew had straight hair parted in the middle. Maria's looked like you could bury yourself in it and never come out.

"Look, Joel, you want to do me a favor?"

"Yes. Sure. Definitely."

"You go back up there and tell the fat fuck that I said three things. First, he is a fat fuck and he can go fuck himself. Second, if he wants me to come back, he has to apologize for being rude to me. I won't have any man being rude to me. I may be poor, but I'm not trash, and I expect to be treated like a lady. And third, I want a raise. Ten cents an hour more. What the hell, make that 20 cents. And if the fat fuck throws a fit, you tell him that to him it's just 20 cents, but to me it's my life."

I sat riveted, enthralled, studying every inch of her face.

"Tell the fat fuck I earn more than that shorting the customers, knowing which ones don't count their bagels, which ones don't count their change. I'm better than anyone, better than him. Tell him that, and tell him if I don't get my raise, I'm gonna turn his fat ass in. I'm gonna let the whole world know what a lousy cheatin', lyin' fuck he is. You tell him that."

I couldn't believe what I was hearing, but at the same time that my innocence was being shattered, I wanted her even more. She was magic and mystery and possibility. I wanted to kiss her.

"Can you do that, Joel?"

"Yeah. Sure."

I got up to leave.

"Hey, Joel," she said. "Thanks. And thanks for being my friend."

I went back to the bagel shop and stood behind the counter while Herman waited on a couple of customers.

"So what are you standing around for?" he growled at me when there was a break. The only customer in the store was at the dairy case.

"You told me to . . ."

"I know what I told you. What am I, an idiot? What did Maria say? That's what I want to know. You must have found her; you were gone long enough to cross the desert with Moses already. Twice maybe. But I don't see her with you, so I'm wondering why you are here."

"I think she'd come back if you offered her a little raise."

"A raise! She wants a raise!"

The woman at the dairy case froze to eavesdrop better.

"And you," he continued. "What do I care what you think? What I want to know is why Maria is not waiting on customers instead of stuffing pizza in her face."

Herman's intimidation was no match for the electricity of Maria's touch, which still tingled on my skin.

"Thirty cents an hour more," I insisted.

"What! She's crazy! A lunatic, she is! That's highway robbery! Why doesn't she just come down here and clean out the register? It would be the same thing. Or should I just hand over the keys and deed to the business while I'm at it? Thirty-cents-an-hour raise? Why not a million dollars?"

"I think I can talk her down to 20. I think I can get her to accept 20."

Herman calmed at once. His face showed a grudging respect, then a sardonic grin, and he nodded at me.

"He thinks he can get her down to 20? Who asked you to handle my negotiations? Twenty cents. What do I look like, J. P. Mellon?"

I crossed my arms defiantly.

The woman set some cream cheese on the counter and produced a wallet from her purse.

"I'll be with you in a minute," Herman said to her.

There was a loud crash from the rear of the shop, from behind the big door that hid the mixers and bagel machines, and we could hear yelling from back there.

"Look, Joel, I don't have all day. You tell your friend Maria to get her fanny back here now or I'm going to hire somebody else."

The woman cleared her throat and announced, "I'd like a half dozen water and a half dozen egg."

The little bell jingled, and two more women entered the store.

"I'll give her five cents raise," Herman said to me over his shoulder as he plucked bagels from the bins and shoved them into paper bags.

"She wants 30. I think she'll take 20."

"What are you? Her manager? I hope she's paying you well."

I wished she were here watching.

"Okay 10 cents," he said.

"Twenty."

More customers came in. He pushed the bagels across the counter to the woman and swooped up her money. People in line were getting impatient.

"Fifteen cents. My last offer."

I found Maria sitting in the same booth at Giovanni's, still fretting over her nails. She was smoking a cigarette, and I could see lipstick on the filter. She turned her head and blew a cloud of smoke to the side.

"What's tricks?" she said. "Is it getting hot out? It feels hot in here to me."

I sat down opposite her.

"Hey, you want a slice or something?" she said. "I could go for a slice."

"I think we need to get back up there. It's kind of busy and he's getting mad."

She set down her cigarette in an ashtray, lifted her pocketbook off the bench, placed it on the table in front of her, dug out a change purse, unsnapped it, and extracted a dollar. She slid the dollar bill across the table to me.

"Get us each a slice," she said.

I got up.

"And a large Coke," she said, reaching for her cigarette. "We'll split it, okay?"

I had to make a couple of trips, first with the two paper plates, each with a slice of pizza, and then with the Coke. I put the dime change on the table and next to it laid two straws. She unwrapped them, poked them through the plastic lid, drank out of the two of them together and pushed the cup to me, faint traces of lipstick showing on the ends of the straws.

"Okay," she said, "let's get down to business. What'd fat fuck say?"

She picked up her slice, held it above her head, and lowered the point into her mouth.

"He said okay to a 15-cent raise," I said.

I bit into my slice, my eyes focused on the pizza so I wouldn't have to face her as I admitted that I had failed.

"No shit?" she said.

She was smiling. God, she had a wonderful smile. I would have died for her right there and then.

I swallowed too soon and choked. I reached for the Coke and drank before I realized my mouth was on her lipstick. I set it back on the table and muttered, "I'm sorry."

"You're not shitting me?" she said. "He agreed to 15 cents?"

She reached for the Coke, drank, and shoved it back to me.

"I tried for 20, but he'd only agree to 15."

She reached across the table, seized the back of my head, pulled me toward her, and, leaning halfway across the table herself, kissed me on the lips.

"Thanks, Joel," she said. "You're terrific. This is the fourth time I've quit, plus he's fired me twice, and I've never come out of it with a raise before. You're a genius."

She picked up her slice and bit heartily into it.

"Let's go," she said. "I can't wait to see the fat fuck's face when he apologizes to me."

Maria marched up Murray Avenue to the bagel shop and I followed. She strode up to Herman and calmly tied on her apron as he finished with a customer.

The next woman in line started to give Herman her order.

"One moment if you please," Herman enunciated loudly. "Miss Debonna will be happy to take care of you."

Maria stood her ground.

"We got business to discuss," she said.

"The business here is bagels," Herman said, as if to a child. "We sell bagels to customers. This fine lady here is a customer. If you would be so kind, your job is to sell her bagels."

"I don't have all day," the woman said, shaking a list on a little scrap of paper. She was a small thing with a pinched-up face, gray hair, and a black hat with a stickpin in it. "I'm double parked. I should get a ticket, who's going to pay? You?"

"Don't you have something to say to me?" Maria said, glaring at Herman.

"We can discuss it later."

"I want half a dozen water, right out of the oven . . ." the woman commenced her list.

"Then I can start working later," Maria said.

"This is your fault," he said to me.

"Half a dozen egg . . ."

"You leave him out of this."

"Young lady, don't you raise your voice to me."

"Half dozen sesame . . ."

"That does it."

Maria untied her apron and stripped it off.

"Is anyone listening to me? I'm double parked."

Herman and Maria were locked in a stare-down.

"I got it," I said.

I found a paper bag under the counter and started fumbling bagels into it.

"Make sure they're fresh," the woman said. "And I want separate bags. Don't mix the sesame with the water and the eggs. And I want a half dozen fresh bialys in a separate bag."

"I'll give you a nickel raise," Herman proffered.

I stopped what I was doing and turned to him.

"Ten cents," he said.

I was angry now.

"All right already, Jesse James. Highway robbery. Fifteen cents. There. You happy? Done. Now can we all get back to work?"

I finished putting the water bagels and egg bagels into a bag and held it out to Maria, who hadn't budged, her apron still in her hands.

"Don't you have something to say to me?" she demanded of Herman.

"What? Now what?"

He raised his hands to the heavens.

"I got to get permission from the pope or something? Get Jesus to bless the 15-cent raise?"

Maria's eyes were fixed on mine now.

"What about the apology?" she said.

"Oh damn," the woman said. "A cop."

She scurried out the door toward a policeman by a Cadillac double parked in front of the store.

"I didn't ask about that," I said. "I thought the money was more important."

Disappointment, disillusionment, betrayal—Maria's face was more sad than angry, as though she was used to this. She had expected no less, but she had hoped for more. She had hoped for more from me.

I felt so stupid. So small.

"So what's all this?" Herman sneered. "A rift within the union? Mister big-shot manager let you down, little girl? So now can we go to work? Joel, you come with me and we'll start you on the mixer. I'm sure such a smart boy can clean a mixer till it sparkles."

Out on the sidewalk, the woman gestured frantically as she argued with the cop. He attended her stoically and wrote her a ticket.

Herman was near the rear of the store.

"You coming already?" he beckoned. "I'm not paying you a $1.35 an hour to gawk at the pretty girl. Two hours you wasted already. You want I should have to fire you on your first day?"

"I'm sorry," I said to Maria, who was with another customer.

"It's okay," she said as she took the woman's money. "Don't worry about it."

"You coming?" Herman yelled.

"Still friends?" I asked Maria.

"Yeah. Sure," she said, not bothering to look at me.

In the back, behind the big door, I learned how to clean out a mixing tank after the hundreds of pounds of dough were removed. It was over a hundred degrees in that room, and I had to scrape out the tank with a squeegee and then wipe it down with oil. Crawling into that tank was a hard, hot, disgusting job, as were all the tasks that went into making bagels.

I worked at the bagel shop through August. I had to be there at five thirty in the morning. Maria didn't start till eight, and by then I was in the back room covered with sweat and flour. When I left in the middle of the afternoon, she was busy with customers.

The Friday before Labor Day was the final day of my bagel-making career, and I had planned to ask Maria to Giovanni's for a slice of pizza. But she was off, and I had no idea of how to get in touch with her, so I didn't get to say good-bye.

I entered my senior year in high school with grades and college applications to worry about and girls in miniskirts to chase after. I figured I would quickly forget about Maria, but I was wrong. I kept picturing her sitting across from me in the pizza shop, her finger tickling my arm, and I wanted to be with her again.

I called Bagel Macher. Someone else answered. I hung up. I tried again another day. And another. Finally, one day I worked up the nerve to ask for her.

"She don't work here no more," the woman at the other end of the phone said.

"When did she quit?"

"Who is this?"

"Joel. I used to work there."

"Oh yeah, Joel. How are y'uns? This is Lois. I started in August right before you left, remember? When Maria was on vacation?"

"Yeah, sure," I lied.

"Herman fired her," she said.

"He was always firing her. Didn't she come back?"

"Not this time. This time was really it."

"What happened?"

"You're not gonna believe this. You know that rule he has about no collect calls?"

"Yeah."

"Well, one day Maria's working up here and all hell's breaking loose. Herman is out of town and Maria is in charge—he'd made her sort of like assistant manager or something, and whenever he wasn't here, she was in charge—and the phone rings and it's the operator saying she's got a collect call from Herman, and Maria thinks about that for a minute and says you know what the hell, a rule's a rule, and the rule is no collect calls, so she tells the operator she can't accept the charges and she hangs up. A minute later, the phone rings again and it's Herman and he's really pissed. I mean I was all the way over by the oven, and I could hear him screaming through the phone about fuck this and fuck that and who do you think you are and I'm still the boss around here and how dare you not accept a call from me.

"So of course, Maria is really pissed and she's about ready to walk out the door anyway and then the next day the phone rings and it's the operator saying she's got a collect call from Herman, so Maria says yeah okay, I'll accept the charges and again I can hear him screaming through the phone and the first thing he tells her is that she's fired for accepting a collect call, which he's told her a thousand times she's never to do. Now he is a weird fuck, that's for sure, and I expect that he's jerking her chain 'cause he likes doing that, but she's had it with him this time, so right in the middle of his yelling, she hangs up on him, takes off that apron, tosses it on the counter, and is out the door. Came back to pick up her last check and that was that.

"He seemed to know he'd done it this time and didn't bother trying to get her to come back. But just between you and me, Joel, I think she was ready to quit anyway. She's got this new boyfriend, and I think they're getting pretty serious, and I think he's gonna' give her the money so she can go to beauty school. That's what she wanted, you know?"

I don't get back to Pittsburgh much anymore, but business brought me there last month, and I went for a long walk down Murray Avenue to see if any of the old shops were left. Where Bagel Macher used to be is a Rite Aid now. I stopped a passerby and asked what ever happened to the bagel shop.

The man shook his head sadly.

"Closed up years ago," he said. "Couldn't compete with the chains. These young folks don't know a bagel from a hamburger bun. Can't even get a decent bagel in Squirrel Hill anymore."

I stared at the rows of shampoos and deodorants and thought about Maria.

I think about her often. I think about a lot of people from my past. It's just sort of an inventory I go through, an inventory of things lost, and she's on it.

It's not that I want to see her now. I want to see her then. I want to see each of them then, whenever then is.

Going through the inventory leaves me with a vague emptiness, but it's not unpleasant. Happiness lost has a sweetness all its own, because, for me at least, the joy of the memory is stronger than the pain of the loss.

The tingle of Maria's finger on my skin is a remembered delight. So brief. Long lost. But it's in my inventory of happinesses. I said good-bye to the Rite Aid, felt the sweet, vague emptiness, and found myself smiling as I walked up the hill.

I COME FROM

Dana Stewart

I come from a long line of women
who were heads of households.
Not to say there were no fathers present,
but momma's word was law.
There was no back talk or sass.
That could lead to a smack on the ass.

No excuse for chores undone
or homework incomplete, not if you wanted to sleep.

They say I am just the same
Don't give me excuses for half-done things.
I come from a firm hand and a gentle kiss.
A hug even when you weren't down, but because you exist.

Every Sunday morning in church,
momma sang in the choir
watching for your best behavior, with eyes of fire.

Coming of Age

Where Sunday nights saw Disney TV
and *Voyage to the Bottom of the Sea.*
I come from baths every night,
Mr. Bubbles made bathing fun and bright.

I come from wafer cookies and milk at grandma's house,
Where a report card was as good as money in the bank.
I come from a place where individuality was prized,
and self-expression was a gift, shining bright in your eyes.

Where the smell of books old and new, perfumed the room
stacked high along back bedroom walls
and cabinets in the halls.

I come from children told to go out and play, but
be home before sundown, every day.
I come from fresh apples for breakfast,
off trees at grandma's house, lunches with headcheese and souse.

I come from kindness to strangers, from an extra plate at the table,
the belief that there was always one less fortunate, less able.

I will not forget the lessons I've learned
On life where I come from; smiles and conversations.
Like lightning bugs at night over an open field; a childhood delight.
Golden flickerings like earthbound stars, captured and displayed in
empty Miracle Whip jars.

On days when life feels like a struggle
It may take a moment or two,
Then I remember where I come from,
I get myself together and push on through.

BOMBS AWAY!

Mark Williams

Scrunched one June night between Helen Clark's screened window and the Clarks' hydrangeas, their deep blue blossoms the size of his buzzed head, 14-year-old Wendell Stone watched Helen's nightgown drop. It seemed wrong, somehow, to think of her in ways that he'd been thinking—Helen, who, like the Clarks' hydrangeas, had bloomed, too. Until that spring, Wendell had thought of her as an adequate right fielder in neighborhood baseball games, someone who played H-O-R-S-E with him when neither Winky Dinks nor Jack Frary could shoot hoops. She had a decent chest shot.

But that night, as Wendell's eyes involuntarily followed Helen's nightgown to the blue-green shag, the room went dark—Helen's ballerina lamp chain pulled. *Chank-chank.*

Through the static on Helen's bedside radio, the Everlys sang about crying as Wendell ducked below the sill and snuck behind the hydrangeas, cracking his head on a silent window air conditioner along the way. Head throbbing, he jumped on his Huffy, hidden behind the Clarks' garage, and pedaled home.

"What do you think of Helen?" Wendell asked Winky one night that fall. The two boys had walked to the end of Wendell's street and were nearing the grassy top of Sled Hill—Wendell in front, Winky trailing.

"You mean like—as a girl?" asked Winky.

Turning toward Winky, Wendell saw the lights from their neighborhood, Saint Lawrence Court, below. Beyond that, across the Ohio River from Clarksville, the Louisville skyline gleamed. "Sort of," he said.

But before Winky answered, just as they reached the hilltop, they saw what they had come for, shining in the northern sky and arcing east. "There it is!" said Wendell. "Sputnik!"

"The commies put a dog inside," said Winky, right eye twitching in the moonlight. But by the time they started down Sled Hill, the thought of Helen had resumed its orbit inside Wendell's head.

That winter, as the world grew colder, Wendell and his classmates ducked beneath their desks. One morning, from beneath the desk in front of Wendell, his buddy Jack turned toward him and whispered, "Hey, Wendell, my brother Larry's got an idea."

"Silence!" said Miss Berman.

After school that day, Wendell, Jack, and Winky met Larry Frary in the parking lot at the Dairy Barn on Clark Street. Leaning against his yellow Olds, a Super 88 with whitewalls, Larry took a drag from his Camel and said, "You little cats steal stuff. I haul ass to Hock and Shop. After one of you steals five hundred dollars' worth a shit, that fucker's in."

"In what?" asked Winky.

"The Five Hundred Dollar Club, moron!" said Larry, flicking his Camel to the pavement, then grabbing another from between his ear and greased-back hair. "Then he and I split five hundred fifty-fifty."

As far as Wendell could tell, it should be called the Two Hundred Fifty Dollar Club. And it was stealing. But Jack and Winky were cranked. And maybe this is what you did to get an Olds.

"Stick to small stuff," Larry said. "Hock and Shop won't ask no questions."

By June, Jack was only five dollars shy of his five hundred. With Wendell distracting a Western Auto salesclerk in aisle two ("Would you recommend a Delco or this Champion spark plug, sir?"), Jack entered the store. Thanks to a Swiss Army knife in aisle seven, Jack was first to enter the club. Two hundred fifty dollars richer, Jack treated Wendell to a chocolate Milkmaid at Dairy Barn for his help.

With Wendell eighty dollars short of his five hundred, Winky was barely halfway there. Winky had last tried to snatch the green Sylvania radio from Shangri La, his family's Ohio River camp—a mobile home on stilts.

Wendell had been at Shangri La that day with Winky, their bikes propped against a sycamore tree, its roots descending down the bank into the river. Standing lookout at the knotty-pine-framed door, Wendell was thinking that the sycamore leaves looked like green, five-fingered infield gloves, that the sycamore balls hanging from the tree looked like little baseballs, when he felt his sneakers tremble.

"Do you feel that?" asked Wendell, turning toward Winky.

"What?" asked Winky, crossing the kitchen's checkerboard linoleum to the counter, where the green Sylvania stood.

"This shaking, I feel it in my feet."

"That's just you, candy-ass," said Winky. But then, as Winky reached across the counter for the plug, all of Shangri La began to shake.

"It's an earthquake!" cried Wendell as the kitchen cabinet doors flung open, a blender blasted off the counter, and a framed photograph of President Eisenhower flew off the wall, missing Winky's head by inches.

"Let's get out of here!" cried Winky, jumping over his father's yellow Naugahyde recliner as it moved from the living room into the kitchen.

After that, Winky lost his nerve.

These bomber wings must be worth ten bucks, thinks Wendell, rummaging through Helen's parents' dresser.

Minutes earlier, he'd eased through Helen's window, intending to snatch her radio. That day at Shangri La had given him the idea. Besides, with the way the Everlys had sounded, she could use a new one. Crummy as her radio is, it would still be worth five dollars. Then, when he joined the club, he could buy her a good one. But standing by her bed, reaching for her Philco, he could not steal from Helen. Still, he might as well have a look around, he thought—starting with her parents' bedroom.

Seventy dollars to go, thinks Wendell as he walks down the hall and returns to Helen's room, her father's Army Air Corps bombardier wings in his right pocket.

Her room is dark. He'd yanked the ballerina's chain after entering Helen's window, so no one could see him snooping. But with the air conditioner in her parents' room rumbling like a B-17, he does not hear the Clarks' DeSoto. He does not hear their kitchen door.

"What a great movie!" a man's voice—Mr. Clark, Wendell figures—booms from somewhere. "*Damn—*"

"Language, William."

"No, Marge, *Damn Yankees!* Sure glad it was playing at The Moonlight."

"Helen, it's past your bedtime," Helen's mom says.

"It's barely eleven o'clock," whines Helen. "I'm practically 15. Gee whiz, Mother!"

"Whatever Hel-en wants," sings Mr. Clark.

William Clark, distant relative of Revolutionary War hero and town namesake, George Rogers Clark, had once worn his bombardier wings to a July Fourth neighborhood cookout.

"I was a bomber in the big one, son," he'd told six-year-old Wendell. "When I was stateside, we flew a practice run from our base in Dyersburg to Louisville. When I saw the spires at Churchill, I dialed the altitude, wind, and speed into my sight and caught the airplane plant in crosshairs. Took out four C-46 Commandos," he said, fingering the winged bomb above a splotch of ketchup on his T-shirt. "When we turned back, I had our pilot tip a wing to Marge. Later that year we made Helen. Bombs away!" he shouted, heading for the grill.

For years, Wendell thought the old blowhard had dropped bombs on Louisville—that it had contributed, somehow, to Helen.

"Goodnight, Mother. Goodnight, Daddy."

"Sleep tight, don't let the bedbugs bite!" shouts Mr. Clark as Wendell, who can't believe he shut Helen's window after entering, scurries under Helen's bed.

"Oh, Daddy. *Here*, Miss Kitty," calls Helen.

At any other time, Wendell would have had visions of *Gunsmoke's* Miss Kitty. She has a classy chassis. He suspects she offers Marshall Dillon more than drinks. But here beneath Helen's bed, chin on shag, Wendell remembers seeing a calico cat run from Helen's room as he'd eased into her window. Peeking out the space beneath the ruffle, Wendell sees this Miss Kitty trot from the dimly lit hall into the bedroom on the heels of Helen's Oxford saddles. "There's my good kitty," says Helen, *chanking* the ballerina's chain, then lifting Miss Kitty from view.

"Between a Rock and a Hard Place? Try Stone!" goes Wendell's father's insurance company jingle. The jingle has never made much sense to Wendell. But as Helen's Oxfords turn—heels toward him—and the springs above his head dip slightly, Wendell gets the first part.

"Mommy has to take her shoes off, my little sweet," trills Helen. "Does umms want to hear some moosic?"

"*Now!*" meows Miss Kitty.

Wendell has never heard Helen talk like this: baby talk—and to a cat. And he's never heard a cat cry, "*Now!*" Nor has he ever been this close to Helen, aside from a fortuitous bump while playing flashlight tag in the Saint Lawrence churchyard. I better hold my breath. She could feel me breathing on her legs, thinks Wendell, staring at the strip of flesh between bobby socks and blue-jean cuffs.

"Helen! Turn that radio off!" yells Mrs. Clark.

"But it's Ricky Nelson!" cries Helen.

"I don't care if it's Tennessee Ernie Ford. Time for bed!"

"Just one song, Mother, please," pleads Helen, her socked feet swinging from view, leaving only shoes in front of Wendell.

"Okay, one song."

"Hel-en gets," chimes in Mr. Clark.

With that, Helen jumps onto the floor and blue jeans puddle around her ankles. Bare ankles! True, with Helen this close to the bed and Wendell confined to the floor, he sees less of her now than at the city pool last week. Part of him is saying, *Step away from the bed!* while the other part is saying, *I should close my eyes.* But before she steps away or Wendell closes his eyes, Helen leaps into the air, the box springs sink, and with a *chank,* her room goes dark.

Earlier tonight, about ten o'clock, Wendell had told his parents he was bushed, that he was turning in. "I'm gonna get some shut-eye."

"All right already," his dad had said, rocking in his rocker, flipping through *Time.*

"Let me feel your forehead, hon," said Wendell's mother.

Lying under Helen's bed, Wendell is certain his parents had not heard his bedroom window creak. He'd waited a good five minutes before jumping into the viburnum, sneaking into his garage, and jumping on his bike. His parents wouldn't miss him until morning. With this thought, Wendell lifts his chin from the shag and rests his right cheek on the bridge of his laced fingers. When Helen goes to sleep, he'll slip out. No sweat. Until then, he might as well get some shut-eye.

"Goo-night, my little," says Helen.

"*Now!*"

In Wendell's dream, he's falling through the night sky on the bombardier wings in his pocket. *Either I've shrunk or the wings are ginormous!* Dream Wendell thinks, legs astride the bomb, silver wings on either side. Un-flapping. In the darkness, it's impossible for him to gauge how high he is or how quickly he is falling—or where he's headed, breaking through clouds he had not known were there.

From this distance, Dream Wendell can make out three clumps of light. Somehow, he knows the clump to his left is Cincinnati. The clump to his right: Naptown. Straight ahead is home. Dream Wendell hopes he doesn't land in Naptown. Except for the Indy 500, who would want to land there? he thinks, fidgeting atop the bomb. But glancing down at Naptown, he leans to the right, and by gosh he's heading for Naptown! Shining ever brighter as he falls.

With his newfound sense of navigation, he leans to the left. Somewhere in that clump lies Crosley Field. Though he has no way of knowing what time it is (other than nighttime), he suspects Crosley Field might be contributing to the light-clump. The Redlegs might be playing. He could land at second base beside Johnny Temple. If these are Bill Clark's actual wings (about two inches from silver tip to tip), no one, not even Johnny, will notice. Unless he hits Johnny Temple. After all, he's still getting the hang of navigation, and these little wings (if they are little) are *sharp*. And what if the wings are ginormous and he hits Johnny? In fact, if they're ginormous, he's more apt to hit Johnny. Aside from Johnny, the Reds are weak at second base. Straightening, then leaning slightly forward on the wings, he heads for home.

"*Now!*"

Dream Wendell would expect the wind to sound more like *whoosh* than *now*. And he'd expect it to sound louder. For that matter, why does he only feel the wind on his left ear? Why not his right ear? Why not his face?

"*Now!*"

As if in answer to the wind's demand, Louisville separates into a clump of Louisville on one side and a clump of Jeffersonville, Clarksville, and New Albany on the other—separated by a barge-lit Ohio River. He leans to the right, toward that clump's center.

"*Now!*"

Wind-sound increasing, the Jeffersonville-Clarksville-New Albany light-clump breaks into hundreds. Then, quickly, thousands—the lights of individual houses coming closer. Closer! How is he going to stop this thing? Do I pull up on this? he thinks, gripping the bomb's nose just as Saint Lawrence Court, and, in the center, Saint Lawrence Church, and, in the center of that, the Saint Lawrence Church steeple—way pointier than expected!— looms immediately below.

"Holy moley!" Wendell shouts.

"*Now!*"

A veteran dreamer, Wendell decides this would be a good time to wake up, what with the annoying wind, looming steeple, and scratchy—sandpaper? sanding his left cheek.

"*Here*, Miss Kitty!" a voice cries from somewhere.

"Helen?" Wendell blurts, eye to cat eye.

Thirty years later, Mr. and Mrs. Wendell Stone, taking a canasta break with Jack Frary and his young wife, Sherry, will reminiscence about that summer night in '58. Only then will Wendell learn that Bill Clark, while taking a walk along the river, had once found a frightened young cat.

"Daddy stepped into a groundhog hole. When he stepped out, out popped Miss Kitty," Helen, a large but still attractive woman, will inform Jack, Sherry, and Wendell. "She always slept under my bed. It was like a hole to her. But that night, there was you-know-who."

"Hi, Wendell," answers teenage Helen from above.

"Wh—, where am I?" says Wendell, disoriented from his dreamy fall through space.

"Underneath my bed."

"Oh," says Wendell as the springs above his head shift slightly. "What am I doing here?"

"Robbing us, I guess. I know about your stupid club. But why did you yell holy moley?"

"*Ouch!*" says Wendell. "That hurts!"

"Feels like sandpaper, doesn't it?"

Thanks to Miss Kitty's tongue, Wendell gathers his wits quickly. If he were to tell Helen why he yelled holey moley, he might spill the beans about the wings in his right pocket. "About a grit P80," Wendell says, drawing from his eighth-grade industrial arts instruction. "How do you know about our club?"

But before Helen can answer, from somewhere in the house, the phone rings. "I wonder who that is?" Helen says. "It's after one o'clock."

"Jeez, Louise!" Wendell says. "One o'clock!"

"I think you fell asleep. *Here*, Miss Kitty."

"Helen!" Mr. Clark shouts, opening the bedroom door. "Wake up. The Stone boy's gone missing! Do you know where he is?" he asks as the room outside the ruffle fills with light and Miss Kitty zips from view.

Forty-five-year-old Wendell, dealing out cards and smiling at 29-year-old Sherry, Jack's third wife, will say, "There I was, under his daughter's bed with his wings in my pocket. Somehow, I knew my future depended on her answer."

"Oh, that's so romantic!" Sherry, patting Wendell's wrist, will say.

"Jennifer! Turn that radio off!" Helen will say to her and Wendell's daughter as music plays from down the hall.

"But it's Bono, Mother!"

"I don't care if it's Julio Iglesias. It's time for bed!"

But tonight, with Mr. Clark outside the ruffle and Wendell's future hanging in the balance, Helen says, "Do you know where Wendell is, Miss Kitty?"

"Listen here, young lady, this isn't funny. His mother went in to feel the boy's head and found his bed empty. The Dinks kid's missing, too. If you know anything . . ." Helen's dad says, his pajama bottoms and bare feet—one foot oddly larger than the other—a foot from Wendell's face.

"Sometimes they ride their bikes to Shangri La," says Helen.

"Shangri La?"

"Winky's river camp."

"Oh, yeah. Thanks, honey. Now get to sleep," Mr. Clark says, his mismatched feet turning toward the door.

"Good night, Daddy."

"Oh, and have you seen my wings? They're missing from my drawer."

"Have you seen Daddy's wings, my little sweet?"

"Very funny. Marge, the girl says they've gone to Shangri La," Bill Clark yells as his pajamas disappear from view and the bedroom door slams shut.

"Shangri La?" Marge Clark says.

Now, beneath Helen's bed for almost three hours, Wendell hears a car honk twice. Sounds familiar, he thinks—neck stiff, cheek raw, right thigh sore from lying on the pin behind the wings. "Bombs away!" Mr. Clark shouts from a distance.

"Why'd your dad yell that?" asks Wendell, turning onto his back, repositioning the wings inside his pocket.

"He says that when he's going somewhere important."

"Oh," says Wendell. "Where's he going?"

"To Shangri La with your dad, genius—to look for you and Winky, thanks to me. First they'll pick up Mr. Dinks."

"How do you know all that? You have X-ray eyes or what?" Wendell asks, staring at the springs between slats.

"I recognized your car honk."

"Oh. Well, I guess I'd better be going," says Wendell, scootching through the ruffle with his heels.

"See you later," says Helen as Wendell stands and turns toward her. Sheet up to her shoulders, cat tail around her neck. "Winky," Helen hisses, "if you're in here, you better get out, too. You had your chance."

"*Sheesh,*" a voice says from inside Helen's closet.

Thirty-one years later, 46-year-old Wendell Stone will find himself parked in a Chrysler New Yorker at the Moonlight Drive-In, alone, watching *Big* while waiting for Sherry Frary to arrive in her Ford Fairmont. Early in the movie, 12-year-old Josh will turn into Tom Hanks, a grown-up, and Wendell will think, This is how it works, remembering how one minute Winky's coming out of Helen's closet, right eye twitching in the ballerina light, explaining how Helen happened to tell him she wanted a new radio only her dad had said, "What do you think I am, a money tree?" and how Winky said he might have let the Five Hundred Dollar Club slip out but just so he could help Helen by stealing her old radio when she went to see *Damn Yankees*, because then her dad might buy her a new Motorola Owl Eyes—where the radio dial looks like one owl eye and the other owl eye is a clock—and the next minute you're parked in the back row of drive-in movie waiting for your old friend's young wife. Up to now, Sherry has only seemed interested in your shoulder, crying on it about how all Jack talks about are horse races and basketball, and how Jack drinks too much, too, "and then he's too tired to, you know, and my looks won't last forever," running her hands down that young, slim body while standing atop first base in the Louisville Slugger museum, one of several places where you'd met: the restaurant at the Brown Hotel in Louisville, where you shared a hot brown; Dairy Barn in Clarksville, where you sipped a Milkmaid from two straws.

Just as Robert Loggia joins Tom Hanks on the giant piano keys to play "Heart and Soul," a blood-red Fairmont will pull up to Wendell's New Yorker. Sherry, radiant in the Moonlight's ambient light, will step from her car into his.

But here in Helen's bedroom, listening to Winky explain himself in a whisper, Wendell thinks he's about the happiest guy alive when Winky says, "Jeez, Wendell, I'm here to swipe a radio, not your girl."

"My girl?" says Wendell, turning toward the bed, where Helen's pulled the sheet over both her head and Miss Kitty's. "Is that right, Helen?"

"The swipe-a-radio part or the my-girl part?" asks Helen.

"The my-girl part, I guess."

"If you say so."

"*So,*" says Wendell, grinning.

"If I were you, I'd pitch a tent in front of the church," says Helen from under her sheet. "Your dad's headlights will shine on you when he comes back from Shangri La and turns onto our street. How much trouble can you get into for camping in a churchyard? *Ouch!* That hurts, Miss Kitty!"

"Can I keep the wings?" asks Wendell.

"Can I still have your radio?" asks Winky.

Leaping into the Clark's hydrangeas, Wendell can't believe his luck: the bomber wings and Helen!

"The tent's in our garage," says Wendell, walking down the street with Winky, who's carrying the Old Philco. "I'll get my bike tomorrow."

Now, inside the tent with Winky, waiting to be illuminated by his father's headlights, Wendell has no way of knowing what lies ahead: that someone (a member of a rival club?) will steal his Huffy tonight; that he will feel a pinprick of guilt every time he hears his father-in-law say, "My wings just flew away"; that stepping into Stone Insurance will place him between a rock and a hard place; that life itself is the spot between a rock and a hard place, that spot no more evident than the Corinthian leather seat of a Chrysler New Yorker. Should I stay or should I go? Wendell will think as Sherry—her see-through blouse doing its job, her hips, susurrating on the seat toward him, doing theirs—opens her full, Fairmont-colored lips and says, "Oh, Wendell, *now!*" and Wendell, reminded of cat, dead for more than 20 years, touches the good-luck wings in his right pocket and sets his sight on Helen, home.

GIRLS ROOM II

Sheri L. Wright

One morning, before first period,
Thelma Ford lit up a joint,
took a hit and passed it to us—
rebellion burning
inside strawberry-flavored paper
you could buy at the 7-11.
I was finally going to
inhale the last taboo
of seventh grade in this stepchild of a town.
And it was only September.

Thelma watched me study the etiquette,
the proper way to toke,
like siphoning hot soup from a spoon,
hold it,
pass it to the next like a secret

Cigarettes had primed my lungs
to take the feral rush of sweetness
before it clawed its way out in a cloud.

Someone opened a window
and we fanned our illegal revolt
into the morning air, still warm with summer,
laughing, laughing because it was funnier than
it should have been, because Erica Johnson's tits
nearly fell out of her halter top, but Joyce Bennet said
that's okay, they never stay in there long anyway.
We all lit up cigarettes to kill the odor.

Thelma laughed at the way my eyes watered,
turned red as maraschinos.
After lunch, she lit up
another strawberry oath for dessert.

"Girls Room II" was first published in *In the Hall of Specters* by Sheri L. Wright, 2018.

COMING
OF AGING

———— ∞ ————

*"An unbidden thrill comes in a gratitude that rises from
living long enough to risk being utterly, temporarily, alive."*

—Steve Jenkinson

IT WAS SO ITALIAN OF MY MOTHER

Joan E. Bauer

She saved your letters. After she died,
I found them in plastic shoe boxes.
Florid script in fountain ink still blue.

Deer hunter, engineer, navy lieutenant,
gambling you could make it as a writer.
Sunday morning in a UCLA classroom,

you found me, writing on a blackboard:
Let me not to the marriage of true minds—
1969. I loved your bemused eyes, robust

frame. An epistolary friendship began.
Why'd she save them? Hated to let go
of anything: daughters, arguments,

family treasures. It helped that you're
Italian. What did I write? I was green
as spring grass & I hardly remember.

Coming of Aging

You wrote about friends & fish poachers,
wine & Hemingway, the Vietnam War.
It seems we wrote about our mothers.

Yours, psychic. Mine, omniscient. Though
I don't quarrel now with her wisdom:
Laugh, the world laughs with you.

Weep & you weep alone. Did I confuse
your letters with romance? Maybe.
But no mistaking the brother-sister tone.

I left for Berkeley & married 'that guy,'
as you called him, then moved to Pittsburgh,
near your hometown. Twenty years ago,

I read that sonnet at his funeral. But now
I'm back in LA, happily coupled & you're
married, with two grown sons. Would you

like to read the letters? Should I send them?
These days, I'm less naive, braver, maybe
more patient. How about you?

Previously published in *Paterson Literary Review*

ALONG CAME A SPIDER

Kimberly Garts Crum

I.

The blue faded cover of the book *Passages* peeks out of the top of a liquor box. My first edition hardback has survived multiple book purges, packed and repacked with each move, stored on high shelves and in dank cellars, in case of renewed interest in its subtitled theme—*Predictable Crises in Adult Life*. Thirty-eight years had passed since I first thumbed through the book's pages, contemplating the decades that stretched luxuriously beyond my horizon. The self-help book was shelved, then boxed and mostly forgotten.

During a recent book purge, I rediscovered *Passages*, and had to pause. The life crisis popularly known as "the empty nest," loomed. I wondered how to prepare for this next crisis of my adult life—a stage I do not remember from my first reading of *Passages*. In its yellowed pages, I find scant mention of the sixth decade of life, until the final pages. Here, the author inserts a stunning declarative: "It is imperative that a woman finds a sense of importance and means of independent survival before the empty nest leaves her feeling superfluous." The author has sounded the alarm. Prepare to be unnecessary, redundant, expendable, and obsolete.

Amazon.com describes Gail Sheehy's 1976 first edition of *Passages* as a "road map of adult life [that] shows the inevitable personality and sexual changes we go through in our 20s, 30s, 40s, and beyond." So, it seems, I have journeyed into "the beyond"—a mysterious life stage for which my only context has been my mother.

When *Passages* was first published, my mother had transitioned from the fabulous 40s to her superfluous 50s. Though she maintained the home fires with panache, she was *not* adept at handling "the change," a euphemism for menopause used by polite women of her generation. It's is an inclusive term, inviting diverse crises to the life-adjustment party.

I cannot ask, but only remember, what "the change" was like for Mom. I will not know if she felt empty when I flew the nest. I cannot know precisely how she adapted to the crisis of old marriage. But my memory of one ordinary evening returns to me, when she tried to share her struggles with me before I wished to listen.

I had arrived home at about ten o'clock from my job at Sears Roebuck. Mom sat in her chair with her needlepoint in her lap. She was tuned into the television, for companionship more than entertainment. My father was on a business trip. My brother was married and living away. We were home alone—a stay-at-home mom and a restless adolescent.

"Look at you! You're so busy. Always coming and going," she said. I dropped the keys to the Chevy Caprice on the front hall table and wandered into the living room on my way to the kitchen. I would like to say that I sensed Mom's loneliness. I would like to say that I became a confidant to the woman who had given me life and clean underwear for 17 years. But I was more interested in nabbing leftover cheesecake from the fridge. I was annoyed by the prospect of a heart-to-heart talk with Mom. I sat down on the arm of the sofa, as a dog does on its haunches, prepared to leap into action.

"I wish I had a job to go to!" she said.

"Why don't you get a part-time job?" I said.

"I can't do that. When your Dad is in town, he likes me to be available . . . and he says I don't need to work."

This would have ended the conversation. Mom was a captive to her generation and her compliant temperament. Indeed, successful men of my parent's generation believed the man would appear a poor provider if his wife worked.

As a young adult, I was sure my experience with "the change" would be nothing like my mother's. I would not succumb to mood shifts, tears, and spontaneous agitation. I would be patient with my husband. I would treasure the fact that my grown children no longer needed me. When the time came, I was proud that my elder daughter had departed for college. And I bragged about my high school daughter's independence. Who would question the value of raising two self-sufficient women? As a Second Wave feminist, I continue to wait eagerly to celebrate the Equal Rights Amendment. I have never been an earth mama wanting to sacrifice myself to childrearing. So, why would the empty nest pose a problem?

I first noticed a dullness of mind and a vacancy in my chest. Others observed this detachment. I remember a stranger at the YMCA who asked me if I was all right. I had been sitting at a weight machine, immobile, staring into space, looking like I had suffered a small stroke. I reassured the woman, explaining I had just returned from taking my daughter to college and was feeling a little sad.

Several years passed, and my younger daughter—the last child—left for college. At first, I was symptom-free. No dull feelings, no momentary out-of-body experiences, no tears, and no imagined catastrophes. It seemed I had escaped the melancholy associated with the emptied nest. Then, Liz transferred colleges, moved to Chicago, leased an apartment, and remained in the city during the summer vacation. For the months of that summer, I was irritable—a moody insomniac lacking my usual sunny view of life, plagued by a shape-shifting anxiety—a voice that was mine and not mine, continually reminding me of countless shortfalls in my career, my body, my husband, my life. For the first time in 20 years, I craved a cigarette.

My anxiety appeared in the ordinary moments. One night, my husband and I sat on the front porch sipping wine, his red and mine white. This had been our habit for 25 years. When our daughters were young, wine and conversation had helped us feel like a couple—a relationship that parenthood had interrupted. Absent now was the need for adult time-out. But the ritual continued.

After a period of twilight silence, I pronounced myself "overwrought." The wrought-iron porch railing probably inspired my word choice. It's a thing of beauty, resembling a series of ocean waves on a suspended century-long journey to crash on some distant shore.

"Overwrought is a bit dramatic, don't you think?" John said.

Actually, I thought, overwrought is exactly the right word. Iron is bent into shape, forged by fire—its shape created by the blacksmith. Iron does not have a will of its own. Do I? There was something pathological about my compulsion to buzz from activity to activity each day, then lie awake for hours each night wondering why I buzz from activity to activity each day.

On this particular evening, I complained about my day—the constant phone calls, the politics of leadership, the college students who studiously avoided completion of assigned homework, the insomnia, and the general lack of appreciation for my service to the world.

"I'm overwhelmed," I said.

"You give yourself away," John said. "Maybe you should stop saying 'yes.' You could spend more time at home."

"Well!" I said. "I suppose you'd be happier if I stayed home, cleaned the house, and had a nice hot meal on the table each night."

"It's not my happiness we're talking about," John said.

I've often thought my husband wishes I were more like my mother. Her towels were freshly fluffed, her napkins ironed, counters and sinks wiped clean, vacuum tracks visible on the carpet, ashtrays empty. She was the model housekeeper whose fork-tender, fall-off-the-bone roasts followed a platter of cheeses served room temperature, with martinis very dry.

"I am not my mother," I said.

"No, you are not."

"I will not be remembered for my housekeeping," I said.

"No, you will not."

Both of us continued to stare into the distance. Cars circled the median slowly searching for parallel parking, and dog-walkers passed our porch.

I knew the list of symptoms for the change—the hot flashes, mood changes, memory lapses, and weight gain. I had not expected the crisis of old marriage. Our union has outlived its evolutionary purpose.

In the beginning, I was attracted to John's intellect and his interest in my thoughts—a rarity among the young men I knew in the 1970s. Within the first hour of our first date, he asked what I thought about gun control. I had no opinion on guns but was pleased at the inquiry. Both of us preferred to skip small talk. In all other ways, we differed—Beatles versus Rolling Stones, Catholic versus Presbyterian, untidy versus tidy, extrovert versus introvert.

The differences have continued in predictable rhythm, illustrated by our morning routine. Each morning, John and I stand at our respective mirrors, our coffee cups brimming, black and steaming, on countertops. His bathroom routine is laborious. Mine is rushed. He rinses and flosses. I brush and spit. He pats his face dry with a washcloth. I rip a towel off its mooring and step into the shower, slamming the glass door behind me. He hates it when I slam the door. The shower steams the room. He turns on both the fans, in the water closet and the bathroom.

"It sounds like a jet engine in here," I yell from the shower. He does not respond. I tell John he has a hearing problem. He says I mumble.

"Don't you need some light in there?" he yells.

"No," I say at top-of-voice. "I like it hot and dark."

We have been married 30-plus years, a lengthy duration by anyone's standards. We have raised two daughters, three dogs, three cats, and one ferret. We have raised each other. Now what?

Years ago, in my pre-married life, while in graduate school, I interned with a family therapist who shared wisdom about marriage. "The qualities that attract a person to a mate," she said, "are the same qualities that are most annoying once married." John's spontaneous dry wit, his charming German obedience to rules, and his extraordinary intelligence now annoy me.

My crisis peaked the first summer that neither of my grown daughters came home. One hot July day, I pulled weeds in a community garden with a 70-year-old friend. I confessed to her what I had not admitted to myself.

"I don't know what's wrong with me; I feel so angry."

"Hmmm," the woman said with authority, neither proposing a problem nor solution. I needed no response. I had wanted to say what was obvious to everyone around me—I had become restless, critical, and labile. My life had changed in estrogen and purpose. I could adapt to the estrogen deficiency. But how might I adapt to the change in life purpose? I confronted a dichotomy of feelings—wanting to feel needed and needing to escape. One thing was certain. Neither of my grown daughters would return to the nest. I would have to find a way to be more comfortable with the extra wiggle room or fly away.

II.

"I thought that writer-in-the-woods thing was only in the movies," our pet sitter said as I explained how to feed the cat. I would travel to meet a few writer friends in a four-bedroom cottage by Lake Michigan. It would be an idyllic retreat, in which we would write in the morning, explore in the afternoon and read aloud in the evening.

On the first hour of the first day of my retreat in a charming fishing village turned resort, I sat down on a rise on the beach and wrote in my journal:

> If bodies of water had a gender, the ocean would be male,
> and the lake would be female. The ocean is a roaring foaming
> opaque thing. Lake Michigan seems feminine—soft, quiet, and
> transparent, and so clear you can see the smooth rocks beneath.
> Even the rocks have rounded edges formed by millennia of the

water's embrace. The sunshine creates a honeycomb pattern on the surface, which shimmers in its undulating mirror of water.

This is a place where you could find yourself, if you were lost.

In this place of ponderous beauty, I was alone with the water and the big sky. I could see my writer friends in the distance, walking the beach. It was one of those perfect moments, when you realize peace is possible. Then my cellphone rang. Life once again reminded me of its reality—everything is often fine, until it's not.

My neighbor Maria's voice was breathless. "Something is terribly wrong with Whiskers. She is stumbling around by my fountain, trying to get a drink. She has a black lump on her neck and . . . and . . . there are flies all around her."

I called the veterinarian, who deduced Whiskers was infested by maggots. "Have someone bring her in right away," she said.

Maggots? I remembered my days as a social worker at a burn center, where I learned that maggots—fly larvae—were once used to debride wounds. Dead biological matter is mother's milk to maggots.

"Sounds like a brown recluse," the vet said. A spider bite resulted in necrotic tissue, inviting the maggots to banquet.

Quickly, I returned to the cottage, where I would coordinate cat rescue and veterinary care. Cell reception was fickle there, so I walked the property until I discovered a place with a strong signal—a tree stump. Often, in the next few days, I stood at the stump, making phone calls while my writing friends were sprawled on couches with laptops, glasses of wine, books, and poetry.

Neither the pet sitter nor I knew how badly Whiskers would smell.

"We had to clean out the maggots," the vet said. "The smell was awful. One of our techs threw up. But we've got Whiskers cleaned up now." She hesitated. "She's a very sick cat. We'll see how she does overnight."

The necrotic tissue on Whiskers' neck extended all the way to her jugular. They had to debride the wound completely; the area remained vulnerable. The vet described a two-by-one-inch section of naked dermis, giving Whiskers' neck the appearance of a raw chicken breast.

It is hard to avoid cliché, when your daughter's favorite animal is likely to die, and you know she will blame you, and you are ashamed because you resent your daughter's cat for interrupting your idyllic writing retreat.

"Keep her comfortable. Don't take extreme measures. I don't want her to suffer. She's an old cat," I said.

I called John, who was out of town, to inform him of Whiskers's injury. I asked him to call Liz. "I can't talk to her. I'll cry. She doesn't need to hear me cry." Then I continued to participate in the retreat whenever I was not standing by the tree stump to negotiate cat care. Though I attended our book discussions and readings, I could only focus on one scene with two characters—John is on the phone telling Liz in his matter-of-fact manner, "I'm afraid I've got some bad news. Whiskers is very sick. She might die." Liz refuses to weep. Stoicism is her inheritance.

Liz called next day to ask for plane fare. She would be flying home. "I want to be there," she said. We both knew her reason for the journey. She expected death. Liz flew from Chicago to Louisville. She sat with her cat, feeding Whiskers fingertips of deli turkey. And, after two days of IV fluids and antibiotics, it looked like Liz's cat would survive.

John and I talked by phone about the cat's progress and our daughter's mental health. We discussed the immediate future—how we would have to do twice-daily dressing changes, how Whiskers would need one to two more surgeries to close the wound. John did not debate the need to spend more than $1,000 on veterinary care. We laughed together at discharge instructions that advised, "Keep your pet from jumping or climbing stairs." We housed the cat in a dog crate to make sure she would be quiet. For several weeks, I extracted her from the crate once daily, laid her across the kitchen counter, and medicated and changed the gauzy bandages around her chicken neck. She was a wounded warrior—defeated by the freedom of her outdoor pursuits, resigned to her fate, too tired to resist wound care.

I was gratified by my job as cat nurse and sensed a subtle change within. Absent was the disembodied anxiety. Absent was the irritation or dissatisfaction with life and marriage. During the time Whiskers recovered, I was essential, not superfluous. Of course, my new purpose in life was transient. The cat would heal and live another year. The daughters would continue to shape their lives independently. John would continue to be the man he had always been—my tender opposite. Life would revert to the new normal. And I would have to invent ways to avoid feeling unnecessary, redundant, or obsolete.

I scorn the adjective "superfluous." In order to escape its grip, I must determine its full definition. I find the answer in my favorite self-help book—the *Oxford English Dictionary*. The OED defines "superfluous," as "unnecessary; especially, being more than enough." The Latin root is *superfluus*, which means "overflow."

Ah yes, my nest overflows—not with children, but remembrance, accomplishment, wisdom of the world, a sustaining marriage, and two adult women who exist because of me/because of us. My purpose in the world has shifted. I might even be unnecessary. But I am "more than enough."

First published in *The Louisville Review* literary journal, Spring 2016

WISH YOU WERE HERE

Karen George

I'm first in line to cross the Ohio.
A barge, piled with coal, churns
water white. In fields birds sway
shriveled Queen Anne's Lace
and dark sumac, pick through flood debris.
With binoculars I spot
large nests near tops of sycamores.
Redbuds fleck the hills purple and white.
The air muddy, fertile.

The man motions me onto the ferry, all way
to the metal chain—links big as my fist. A quiver
prickles behind my knees, to see the river
rock a few feet from my bumper.
Rust coats every surface.
The worker palms my dollars,
asks how I am but doesn't wait to hear.

When the gangplank scrapes concrete,

I drive onto solid ground,

and on the radio an acoustic guitar strums

the opening of "Wish You Were Here,"

notes that never fail to trigger shivers.

How I miss sitting beside you

when we climbed out of river valleys.

Included in *Swim Your Way Back* (Dos Madres Press, 2014)

THE CERTAINTY OF HARD CHAIRS

Lennie Hay

Baby and I drive 45 miles on a cold Saturday. Baby will be welcome. I know, because I called ahead and asked about dogs. Tyler, my son, has been in residential drug treatment for three weeks. I know because the staff called, with his permission, when he checked himself in. We can stay no longer than two hours. Rules for visitors came in a letter. No packages. No handbags inside. No phone calls. Everyone must leave by 3:00 p.m. But dogs are welcome with advance notice. I am glad to be certain of these things.

I sit on an old unpadded dining room chair at the border of a large room for visitors and wait. Eighty-pound Baby sprawls at my feet. I assume my son will sit in the empty straight-backed chair next to me whenever he arrives from wherever he is. When he appears, framed in the doorway, he seems taller than a few months ago, probably because he has lost weight. His jeans hang loose, pleated around his waist by a belt. I take in all the data about my son, register it in some file. Baby, big lummox of a dog, dances with delight. I stand up awkwardly, knock over my chair, clatter of wood on wood. Nothing damaged. No one broken.

My eyes and nose seep, and I wonder if I should find a Kleenex. He speaks quietly, fills a chilly silence. *We do everything here. Cook, clean, wash clothes. No bleach. My tighty-whities aren't so white anymore.* He makes me laugh. Now I know something about his life here. He lets me reach up and touch his smoothly shaven cheek, leans close to me, and receives my hug. I feel thin broad shoulders, his strong chest when I clasp him to my breast. I seek assurance; I need proof of his being. We turn our chairs to face out a window, let an imaginary veil of privacy drop, separate us from other family reunions. I struggle for words. Normal words. I make sounds—sports teams, his dad's projects, my job. Unsure of what should come next, I blurt: *How would you feel about moving home?* His clear hazel eyes meet mine and his words stretch between us: *I don't know how I feel about much of anything. I've been high or trying to get high for half of my life. Thinking about my feelings, a future—it's all new to me.*

He knows chills, fever, vomit, malaise, waking lonely, here, safe in a clean bed. He drops his hand to pet his dog, so I join him, place my hand on his. Sweet memories. Stone-cold memories. Sirens. Singing. Giggles. Shrieks. *How does he feel?* A child asleep on the bottom bunk. A stranger in my home. I am unsure about this evening, next week, but I am certain some things must be—a mother holds and rocks her child. Sings him to sleep. Forgives him. We sit in silence, grow accustomed to the unyielding chairs.

HAIR PEACE

Bonnie Omer Johnson

"You have a thick fringe around the sides of your head; as a result of aging and loss of estrogen, you have male pattern baldness." My gentle, youngish dermatologist leaned against the cabinet in the examining room, crossed his arms, and offered the unsettling diagnosis for the hair loss I had experienced across the past six months.

I knew about menopause. Other than being wackier than usual and becoming a walking space heater strong enough to warm an abandoned warehouse, I am happy to have escaped a few difficulties many women my age face. Dryness? Quite the opposite. Crying jags? No more than usual. Lethargy? More like energy surges. Difficulty sleeping? Are you *kidding* me? Fast asleep immediately when my head hits the memory foam pillow where I sleep for six hours as deep as daffodil bulbs in January—or until I need to go to the bathroom. But male pattern baldness? How could I have missed *that* warning?

Two decades ago, I liberated my hair from the torture perpetrated upon it for as long as I could remember. In doing so, I liberated myself from an obsession with hair. I'd been rolled and shagged, bobbed, feathered and pixied, sprayed and teased, air-dried, bonnet-dried, and blown dry. I'd been clipped and pinned, kinked and curled and spit-curled, crème rinsed and conditioned, stripped, dyed, frosted, and streaked. Ahead of my time, I had purple hair—accidentally so by a "temporary" platinum blonde rinse over hair greened by chlorine the summer my natural silver blonde color started to darken. I was 15. Who knows how many years raising hair took from my allotted time on earth? My hair had been pigged and ponied in tails from stubbed to long and swingy. Like a rebellious child, it waved and kept doing exactly what it wanted. Even if I forced my hair into a state of compliance, it wandered its own way in defiance by midday. I complained and worried about its future until I realized my expected life span was dwindling by the hour. It was time to re-evaluate the power I conceded to dressing my tresses. I gave it up like one is supposed to give up the narcissists in life.

I barely make it to appointments—jobs, checkups for medical and dental maintenance, grandchildren's concerts, work, classes, weddings, funerals—and always arrive anxious. Avoiding hair care eliminates or reduces social anxiety, reserving my energy for people-ing I need or want to do—both the dreaded and the delightful.

If, as it's said, "the most important thing a woman can have other than talent is her hairdresser," then I am at the very least, 50 percent deficient. I've had my share of hairdressers. And I like them all. A lot. They are a well-groomed bunch, those hairdressers. I've always found them friendly and service-minded, eager to please. I'm satisfied with their efforts and mostly with their results. Hair waits until a few hours after I leave the salon before the lacquered cowlicks struggle loose, or my hair becomes a disheveled, gluey, gooey—or oily—mess, or is, as Margaret Mitchell says: Gone with the wind.

I've tried all the suggestions. Brushed it a hundred times at night, and before I could do it myself, sat not-so-quietly while an aunt or grandmother brushed it for me. It has its own way now and continues to run amok. We are both stubborn.

If I wanted to waste money, rather than being professionally coiffed, I could throw dollar bills into the Ohio River and watch the current carry them toward the Mississippi. Or I could make purchases from late-night infomercials; I could have bought the Jack LaLanne home gym.

Let me tell you, I paid my dues.

As a toddler, I remember hair being twisted around a strip of fabric that was tied in a knot before going to bed at night. Every night.

Before the sound of breaking glass ceilings echoed across the country and before the Equal Rights Amendment was ratified by 30 states, movie stardom was an opportunity for women to build independent careers and attain personal wealth.

Beauty became an economic commodity. Hair products became a major extension of the nascent cosmetics industry. Not the least of these was the home permanent, and Toni became the leading brand. One of Toni's best-selling products was made for little girls—the Tonette home perm—a regimen of rubber curling rods, little squares of tissue paper, and the foulest-smelling, slimy liquid that set the scalp on fire and squinted the eyes to shut out searing vapors that burned away any nose hairs and practically cauterized the nostrils. In time, the nose hairs grew back.

In my household, growing up, four of us shared a single bathroom. Green tiles up the wall shoulder-high, trimmed in butter yellow subway tiles laid vertically atop the four-inch squares; plastered walls above the tile were painted or wallpapered in various hues throughout the 60 years my parents owned the house. My father was a clean man, always first to shower in the morning. In high school, by the time he had completed his daily routine before cooking a Grand Slam breakfast for the rest of us, I had been up for three hours for my uninterrupted time in the bathroom, for homework, to read, or journal, but mainly, I got up for my hair.

During part of my teens, social status depended on the size of one's hair. The invention of brush rollers and steel combs gave rise to silhouettes that made us appear to be wearing giant pumpkins on our heads. Empty orange juice cans gave some a head start on the "big head."

Gallons of Aqua Net hairspray and homemade concoctions of sugar-and-water setting lotion gave limp-haired ladies new hope for a hairdo that looked as if hair was inflated like a helium balloon. A row of bobby-pin curls around the bottom of rolled hair sprayed stiff gave a desired flip to backcombed hairstyles. Beach movies starring former Mouseketeer Annette Funicello demonstrated that with enough hairspray, the flip stayed perfect even while surfing with Frankie Avalon.

Once bottle brush wire curlers became de rigueur, a kind-hearted woman—you just know the inventor was female—devised rollers made from pink foam with a fold-across snap fastener. Sleeping was far more comfortable. No longer did we have to sleep face down in the pillow. No longer must each curl be attached to our heads by stabbing a plastic sword through the hair and roller to the scalp. The "swords" were like ones used to float cherries in cherry Coke or like ones stuck in a beef steak to mark its degree of doneness.

Resulting hairdos weren't quite as big with the foam curlers because hair wasn't as tight. If a woman of any age left the house on the day she washed and dried her hair, she wore a silk headscarf over her head rather than expose her clips or rollers in public. Thick or longer hair could take up to 24 hours to dry.

Eventually came the home hair dryer in a case like a small piece of luggage. Unlike modern handheld blow dryers, ones of yore consisted of a motor inside a cannister and a large plastic bonnet two layers thick with holes the size of a pencil randomly placed all over the inner layer. The bonnet and motor were connected by an accordion tube similar to ones used on Electrolux vacuum cleaners. With its umbilical cord to an outlet, bonnet dryers opened all sorts of possibilities for efficient time management. We began growing our hair longer. We didn't have to sleep in torturous brush rollers. I could shower, roll my hair, and dry it under the bonnet dryer in a fraction of the time. Women could wash their hair more than once a week or every 10 days. Baby powder or baking soda brushed through locks between washings prior to the invention of dry shampoos kept hair from looking greasy. An old wives' tale warned women and children not to wash hair during the month of February to lessen the likelihood of catching pneumonia.

With the arrival of Peter, Paul, and Mary on the music scene, straight long hair and straight bangs were the "it" hairstyle among young teens. No more Toni perms! The British Invasion brought the Beatles and Herman's Hermits styles akin to a "bowl cut"; a bit later, Farrah Fawcett, Dorothy Hamill, Cindy Lauper, and Jennifer Anniston created new waves of hair envy. We experienced a short-lived resurgence of the perm in the '80s, but before the dawn of the 21st century, I'd sworn off beauty salons, haircuts, twisting, or drying my hair with any kind of electrical device. I had found hair peace.

Let it flow and grow. The occasional bow, banana clip, rubber band, or headband keeps it out of my face. If it gets too wild, I have scissors. Two or three times a year, I coax the ends around a curling iron. I promised Father Time not to waste my allotment of days enslaved to hair. We can peacefully coexist; I wish to continue living under its roof, but I will not give up well-earned liberty from the silly hair practices of days gone. I can't afford the time.

But now? The peace has been disturbed. Tangled by a diagnosis. I think too much about hair. Not *just* thinking about it, but I find myself wondering if the bare white of my scalp is widening, wondering if hair implants are available for women, if they are painful or expensive, and I wonder how vain I must be to wonder. I am tempted to count hairs when I clean my brush or pick hair from the shoulders and collar of my winter coat. I look in mirrors when I pass. Again, I feel concerned too much about appearances. Mine.

I wonder if male pattern baldness is something to get over like a schoolgirl crush—or pregnancy. I wonder if vitamins the dermatologist recommended will successfully show new growth in the suggested three-month trial period, and I wonder if the anti-anxiety herbal tablets I ordered off the Internet calm or even cure my hair obsession. A friend suggested them to me after I shared the diagnosis. Now I wonder if I'll remember to take the vitamins and herbs, but mostly I wonder at how much I'm wondering about hair again.

Dear Nancy,
I hope the joy & love in
my story travels with
you — everywhere!

SIMON AND THE ACTRESS

❧

Mary Lou Northern

Mary Lou

On the last day of the 20th century, a Friday, it snowed. Simon Nelson, age 92, had given his word to the sheriff to meet the three o'clock train. He was to secure the prisoner and take him to the county jail. Simon walked away from his house dressed in his best suit, dress shoes with dress socks, a dress shirt and tie. A windbreaker. No coat. He wore yellow leather yard gloves. No hat. Within minutes, snow studded his silvery hair. His nose and his feet soon smarted from cold. To keep from falling, he took baby steps in the street where car tires had tracked parallel white paths. A man of his word, he would get to the train.

A mile from 5710 Clover Road, his home for 62 years, he encountered a gas and electric man working on a downed line.

"Where're you heading?" the gasman called out.

Simon looked him over, noticed the green logo stitched on his jacket— Louisville Gas and Electric—and decided he was legit. He removed his glove from his right hand and reached for the wallet in the back pocket of his pants.

From the wallet, he took a card and held it for the gasman to read. Simon believed the card gave him the powers of the sheriff's office.

"Honorary sheriff's deputy. The Sheriff's Scholarship Fund," the gasman said. "So, where're you heading?"

Cold air seized Simon's vocal cards, making his voice raspy. "Call the sheriff on your radio. He'll tell you; I'm to meet the three o'clock train."

The gasman looked at the card and then at Simon. "Best put your glove back on."

Keeping his eyes on the gasman, Simon tucked his chin down to keep the falling snow from hitting his face. "Got to secure a prisoner."

"Need to verify who you are," the gasman said.

Simon tried to pull his driver's license from the wallet, but his hands shook. He handed the wallet to the gasman who eased out a thumbed-over snapshot.

"My daughter." Simon pointed a shaking finger at the photo. "Her name's Eleanor. It's on the back." He pushed his hand into the glove.

"Don't you have a coat?"

Of course, he owned a coat. Camel hair. Simon looked down at his windbreaker. Who put that on him? "I need to meet that train."

"Climb in my truck. Out of the snow. I'll take you."

"To the train depot. Tenth Street."

The gasman nodded. He helped Simon onto the truck's running board.

Simon settled into the passenger seat and looked down on the gasman. "Union Station."

"That's a good five-mile walk from here."

Simon nodded.

"That's the bus company. Hadn't been a train there in years."

He wouldn't let this man stop him. "The three o'clock."

The gasman closed the door and went to the driver's side. He drove to the Clover Road address on Simon's expired driver's license. Simon looked at his house. "I said depot, not home. Something wrong with your ears?"

"No, sir." The driveway hadn't been shoveled. He parked on the street.

"I need to get hold of the sheriff. Inform him of the delay."

The gasman aimed the dashboard vent in Simon's direction. "I'll have my dispatcher put a call through." He radioed the dispatcher, gave him a description of Simon along with his name and address. Then he recited the name and number on the back of the photo, saying he would wait with the old man in his truck where it was warm.

"No need to bother Eleanor. You need to get me to the depot."

"We'll wait here," the gasman said. "For the sheriff."

The gasman lit a cigarette.

Simon had always been a pipe man until his daughter nagged him to quit. Nights alone in his bed, he could smell Mixture 79, bought in a tin at Walgreen's, seeping from his mattress along with the rose-scented perfume his wife dabbed on her neck, just below her ear, where she liked to be kissed.

Cigarette smoke filled the cab and the gasman cracked his window. The truck's heater hummed. Simon considered he'd been too quick to trust the fellow. A picture of the gasman with a woman and a girl had been taped to the dashboard. Why did he have a picture of Simon's wife and daughter? Maybe waiting for the sheriff wasn't such a bad idea.

A while later, a purple car pulled in front of the truck and a woman stepped from it in the swirl of a black cape. Simon noticed black boots went all the way to her knees and a long red scarf hung from her neck. What was this woman doing with Laura's scarf?

"That your daughter? Eleanor Nelson?"

"Don't know her." Simon's daughter had red hair, not gray. She didn't wear wire-rimmed glasses. Her cheeks were not jowly, and she didn't have a paunch. "Puts me in mind of Lady Macbeth."

The gasman laughed and opened his door.

"Dad," she said, looking to Simon.

"I found him wandering," the gasman said.

She put her hands to her chest and breathed deeply. "Can you help me get him in the house?"

"Sure, lady." They came around to Simon's side of the truck and opened the door.

"I need to get to the train." Simon noticed the quick exchange of looks between the gasman and this woman as if they knew more than he did. Hah, they wouldn't know what a DeSoto looked like if it ran over their feet. Say icebox to them and they'd look at you as if you'd said mousetrap. They wouldn't know a fox trot from a jitterbug. As far as he was concerned, they knew nothing, not even how to secure a prisoner.

"Dad, we need to go in the house. Get your overcoat and your winter gloves."

"Nothing wrong with my gloves." He looked at his hands. Yellow leather, his yard gloves—what fool dug them out of the closet in the dead of winter?

"Dad?"

Simon didn't like this old woman calling him dad. Would she call him 'pops' next? From the truck cab, he looked down on her, deciding the sooner he went into the house, the sooner they'd skedaddle. Then he'd get to the train in time. He swung his legs around and didn't pull away when she hooked her hand on his arm. He let the two of them guide him across the snow-covered lawn to the porch steps. The gasman's strong hands pressed against Simon's back. "A step at a time," he said.

He'd go along to get along. Done so all his life. Though he'd never traveled to Paris or received any award other than a gold watch from the car dealership when he retired, he'd made a decent living for Laura and Eleanor. They'd gone to a multitude of state and national parks, even a trip to Washington, DC. He considered himself a man not easily hoodwinked. Why else would the sheriff trust him to secure the prisoner?

In the living room, he removed his windbreaker and gloves. He sat in the wingback chair by the fireplace. The woman left the room, returning with an afghan that she spread across his lap. His fingers caught in yarn. She combed his hair with her fingers; he ducked from her touch.

"He likes to maintain a certain dignity," she said. She untied his shoelaces.

His pants were wet halfway up his shin. Had it been raining?

She spoke to the gasman. "Would you like a cup of coffee?"

"No, ma'am." The gasman glanced from her to Simon. "I got a line to fix."

She put her hand to her cheek. "What am I going to do? I've got a show tonight."

"Sorry, lady." The gasman started toward the door.

"A one-woman play. I don't know what to do. I hate to cancel. All those old people—"

"Lady, I got to fix that line." He put his hand on the doorknob.

She stood, and with a grand sweep, removed her scarf.

"Lady Macbeth!" Simon called to her.

"You remember my performance." She smiled. "In Central Park."

"New York City?" the gasman said.

"No. Here. Shakespeare in the Park. Dad, you sat with Mom—"

Mom? Who was this woman?

"—a long time ago."

"Lady, I got to get back to work."

She nodded as Simon struggled to his feet. "Dad, rest. Please."

"Who gave you my wife's scarf?"

"Mom, she—"

Ignoring her, Simon crossed the room and took hold of the gasman's arm. "I have to get my prisoner to the sheriff." Simon sensed he had to up the ante to get this man to give him a ride to the depot. "There's new evidence. Save him from the gas chamber. I gave my word."

Behind him, the woman spoke, her voice shaky. "I didn't realize he'd gotten this bad."

Simon let the gasman lead him back to the chair. "Mr. Nelson, I talked to the sheriff. He asked me to take over. He was pleased you'd gotten that far."

Simon squinted at him. "Show me your badge."

"I'm not a deputy." He tapped his finger against the Gas and Electric Company logo on his jacket. "I do check the gas supply. I can shut it off."

"Well then," Simon said. "Okay, then."

Eleanor thanked the gasman. He left.

Simon reached for his wallet and counted the bills. All singles. All there. He looked to his daughter. "Who was that man?"

A week later, with the new year underway, Simon sat in his wingback chair from 5710 in a single room at the end of a hallway. He hoped the actress told his daughter she'd put him in this joint. He wore a suit and a dress shirt with a tie. Laura's wedding day picture was on the chest of drawers. Sixty-four years he and his wife had shared a bed, a double and then a queen, and now this, a single mattress that smelled of bleach and plastic, not of Mixture 79 and roses.

The edges of his comforter from home puddled onto the floor. On the other side of the bed, the girl worked in the bathroom, making all kinds of noises—flushing, running water, humming all the while. The smell of Pine-Sol filled the room and made him think of the janitor's closet in his grade school. Laura preferred a cleaner that smelled of lemons.

Simon checked his watch. He'd called Yellow Cab. Time to go. He could make it home for lunch with Laura at the kitchen table. Clover Road. He smiled. From the closet, he took his camel hair topcoat and put it on over his suit jacket, then his hat, tugging the brim low. He returned to the chair and pulled on an extra pair of socks. He hated cold feet. Squaring his shoulders, he carried himself tall, so the help would mistake him for a visitor. Not a minute later, his shoulders rounded until he was another bent old man. He trudged onward.

At the front door, he heard the girl call his name. She ran toward him. Even with his weak eyes, he couldn't miss the bounce of Melanie's ample bosom.

"You be going?" she said. "In this cold? Without your shoes?"

He looked down. Who had taken his shoes? "My cab's waiting."

"I done told you, Simon. No cabs'll pick up folk from here 'less the desk makes the call." She hooked her hand around his arm. "We both know nobody made no call for you." She walked him toward his room. "Now one minute I'm cleaning your bathroom and the next minute you're gone. You trying to get me fired?"

Bossy woman, like that actress, but a gentleman kept his thoughts about women to himself.

February, Simon sat in his chair by the window, watching people come and go from their cars in the parking lot. Purple pushed through dirty snow. Violets? He hoped not. To keep them from choking the grass, he went at them in his yard with a vengeance, digging them out with a long-shanked screwdriver because the trowel dug too wide a hole. He narrowed his eyes at the purple. Crocus, most likely, though his eyes had faded so he couldn't be certain.

In his yard, he'd planted a hundred tulips, all colors, but in recent years, they came up red and yellow. He'd planted white and purple irises. Of late they bloomed the color of muddy water. He would dig out the iris and replace them with an azalea bush that would keep its color, coral, the whole of spring. For fall, he would plant yellow and purple asters, surround himself with color, not these tan walls and gray floor.

Somewhere between looking at the crocus and afternoon snack time, Simon fell asleep. When he woke, the actress sat on his bed. She watched *The Ellen Show*.

"Melanie got permission for me to take you for a drive. We have to be back by supper."

Maybe he could talk her into taking him to 5710. She retrieved a coat and hat from the closet. He'd had a hat like it, a fedora with a smart brim. When she handed it to him, he noticed the soiled sweatband. It wasn't his, but he put it on rather than distract her away from taking him home.

"Dad, you look dandy."

Pops, he waited for her to call him pops. His daughter had bright red hair, the bluest eyes, good figure—the spitting image of her mother. He had reason not to call notice to this woman's size or graying hair. She was breaking him out of the joint, Melanie's name for the home.

"Your gloves. In your coat pocket," the actress said.

There they were, black leather, not yellow.

He looked out the window at the passing landscape. Everything wore winter's dirt. Time to think of spring, of new things. They came to a red light in front of Walgreen's.

"How about you take me to that high-end men's store?"

"Brooks Brothers?"

He shook his head and pointed to the drugstore. "That one right there."

She laughed, which seemed an odd response to him.

Inside, he chose a belt, a packet of handkerchiefs, white undershirts, black dress socks, and a tie, though neither the tie nor the socks held the gold threads that marked quality. At checkout, the actress handed her Visa card to the clerk.

"I pay for my purchases," he said.

"My treat."

He didn't like accepting such kindness from a stranger, but he preferred not to have a dispute in front of a clerk. He touched his finger to his hat brim.

Outside, he stood by her car, waiting for the actress to unlock the door. He looked to the red letters on the brick building. Why had this woman brought him to Walgreen's? The joint had all the drugs he'd want and plenty of pills, lotions, even suppositories.

After a while, she turned into a park where blackened snow humped the side of the road. She drove the winding road. Summer evenings he'd drive Laura and Eleanor down River Road to a fish house for sandwiches, a beer for him. He'd talk about the river, asking his daughter each time if she remembered how long the Ohio flowed.

"Nine hundred eighty-one miles," the actress said.

Had he asked her?

"Indians called it Ohio, which means the great river."

How did she get in his head?

"Kentucky owns all the river along its border. To the Indiana shore."

Damn Hoosiers, worst drivers in the world.

The actress reached over and patted his knee.

Hands on the wheel—how many times had he said those words to Eleanor when he taught her to drive?

She pulled the car to the side of the road. "I don't think it's too cold for us to sit for a bit, do you?"

He shook his head.

"The afternoon sun'll feel good." She turned off the engine and climbed from the car. He followed her to a bench that looked over a meandering creek.

Mossy rocks—brown, gray, and green—strung across the water. Brown-and-white mottled bark from a sycamore tree cluttered the ground. Laura liked this spot along the creek where water flowed over rocks. Eleanor used to laugh at his little bark boats bobbing in the riffles. They'd picnicked here. Or

251

had they? The road had never been so close.

He watched the actress pick up bark and break off its edges. He'd learned how to make bark boats from Old Ben, the handyman who had helped around their house when he was a boy. He'd taught his daughter how to make the boats. The actress cupped the bark in her palm to get a sense of its heft, the way Old Ben taught him by the creek, whistling "Yankee Doodle Dandy," and then talking about their bark boats riding creek water to the Salt River and the Salt to the Ohio and the Ohio to the Mississippi and the Mississippi to the Gulf of Mexico and the Gulf to the Atlantic Ocean.

On the bench, Simon whistled Ben's song as he remembered cutting his foot on a broken bottle in the water. Ben had held his red bandana to the cut to stop the bleeding. The actress picked up the notes. How could that be? Had he told her about Ben? His song? He stopped whistling. He stared at the quiet water pooling above the stones before he looked to the actress. She put her nose to the bark in her hand and took a deep breath. She turned her hand over and let the bark fall to the ground.

Tears in her eyes. He took a handkerchief from his coat's breast pocket, handing it to her. He tried to whistle but his mouth had gone dry.

After the actress returned him to the joint, after she left him alone in the room, after dinner, after a fellow with a guitar played for him and the other inmates in what Melanie called the gathering room, he asked her to telephone his daughter, tell her to visit him, tomorrow, the day after, any day at all. The first time he laid eyes on her, in her mother's arms, in the hospital, was 1947. Two years earlier, soon after he had come home from the war, he had married Laura. Now they had Eleanor, the most beautiful baby, though not as beautiful a woman as her mother.

Weeks passed, each more ordinary to Simon than the one before. He wanted to go home, cook a decent meal, sleep, and not hear strange voices call out in the dark. He wanted to smell trees and grass, not shit.

Another Friday, the actress sat on his bed. He considered such behavior unladylike. He pardoned himself and slipped into the bathroom where he combed his hair, did his business, washed his hands, and splashed water on his face. Laura waited for him. He dabbed a little toothpaste on his finger and rubbed it across his tongue and dentures. He opened the door.

She waited on the bed for him in a black robe. She'd always been modest. He'd turn off the light in a minute. He sat next to her and took her hand in his. Gray had come to her hair, tears to her blue eyes. He put his hand on her cheek. She rested her head there. He stood, bending down to kiss her on the neck, just below her ear, on the spot that always smelled of roses. She pushed him away. "Just a little sugar," he said. "Then I'll turn the lights out."

"No, no!" she cried out as she pressed her hands against his chest.

Why did she push him? He took hold of her wrists, trying to calm her.

She fought him. "Don't! Stop!" she yelled.

"Hush now," he said.

The overhead light shot on. Melanie stood in the doorway. "Simon!"

He dropped his hands away from Laura. She fell onto the mattress. Why was she upset over a kiss? Laura had never screamed at him. He stumbled away from her. Melanie rushed to his side. His knees gave way. She helped him to his chair. He watched her go to the bed. What was the actress doing on his bed? Where was Laura?

"He tried to kiss me. My father, kiss me . . ."

Sad sack, get her out of here, he thought but didn't say.

"Sssh, sssh," said Melanie, and then she hugged the actress. "Honey, they mix people up."

Simon didn't want to hear this. "You best both leave," he said.

"He was so strong. If you hadn't come in—"

"I seen it before. Old man gets sex on his mind and he gets stronger 'n an ox."

Sex! He only wanted a little sugar from his wife. Laura, where had she gone? Hiding in the bathroom. The door was open. The light was on, the room empty. Where did they take her? Simon pointed to the door. "Go on with you. Get out!"

The actress shuddered.

Melanie patted her hand. "It wasn't you. You're so far from his mind."

"I need you to call my daughter," he said, shaking his finger at Melanie's back.

Melanie looked over her shoulder at him. "Now you hush, old man."

Friday, Wednesday, Monday, what did the day of the week or the time of the day matter in the joint? He marked Saturdays and Sundays by the number of visitor strolling the hallways. But it was night again. A strange girl sat in his chair. Melanie told him his daughter had paid to have the girl sit through the night by his bed. It was either that or strap him in to keep him from roaming. They didn't want him falling, now did they, she'd said. He liked the night girl. She didn't pretend his memories belonged to her the way the actress did. She didn't talk on and on the way Melanie did. Her English was bad: his Spanish, worse.

In the low glow of the night safety lights, he watched the night girl slump in his chair. Her eyes lowered. Minutes passed. She snored. He wanted her to wake up. He wanted to tell her that between Ben and himself they had seen a century and a half pass, years moving as fast as a jackrabbit. He closed his eyes. A while later, he felt Ben's hand on his shoulder, patting him, though when he opened his eyes it was the night girl's hand reaching through the metal bed rail. He needed to make sure he told Eleanor what Ben had explained to him about the water in the creek flowing into the Ohio and then the Mighty Mississip, to the gulf, to the ocean.

Another Saturday rolled around. Simon asked the actress to drive him to the high-end men's store. He filled his basket with candy bars, shaving cream, a pad of paper, and a package of ballpoint pens. He would write Eleanor about Ben and the creek and the rivers. How much he loved Laura and how Eleanor meant the world to them. He would write before the night girl arrived and again tomorrow. He would ask the actress to mail the letter to Eleanor. At the counter with the actress, he spotted a red bandana, identical to one Ben had wrapped around Simon's bleeding foot. He reached for it, felt its coarse threads. He handed the bandana to the clerk.

"Dad, you bought handkerchiefs a few weeks ago."

It's a bandana he wanted to say, but a gentleman didn't show up a lady in public.

"I really don't think it's you."

What did she know?

BAT WINGS

Leslie Smith Townsend

Google "aging upper arm skin,"
and get *Advanced Dermatology,*
Rapid Wrinkle Repair,
and *Rebuilding Your Arms*
To Get Rid of Batwings.

You know the score—
When a willowy woman walks
through the door and your heart catches
and mind leaps to calibrate envy,
mean thoughts, jealousy,
or at the least, avoidance,
How can she be real?
But she's as real as you and me.
It's beneath the skin that brands her.

Can I be proud of imperfection?
Be who I am without deception?
If I'm full of pudge and thinning hair,
no longer win awards or list accomplishments,
if I'm only there—

invisible to Superwomen,
will you care?
And if not, who will love you
with your illusions of importance
and immortality?

OFFERING

Judith Turner-Yamamoto

Marjorie Norman leaned over the steering wheel, stared at the man asleep on his back on the heating grate. A trio of shopping carts piled high with clothes and blankets circled like wagons against the April chill. A Barbie doll wearing an evening dress lay beside him. The sight was so peculiar Marjorie changed lanes to get a better look, even though the slightest detour during rush hour would mean being late for her appointment at the hairdresser's.

"Why go out now when the rest of the world is on the road?" her husband, Burt, had protested as she left the house this afternoon. She *liked* being caught up in the frenzied movement that every morning and evening gripped all of Washington. Even the Georgetown salon snapped to attention when women arrived from their downtown offices, exhausted but keyed up with an unshakable purposefulness. They informed the receptionist of their tight schedules, questioned a shade chosen by the colorist, sent the shampoo girl scrambling for a glass of wine, mineral water. Marjorie could pretend to have the same urgency.

Horns sounded beside her. The car waiting to turn left at the front of the lane had just cost these drivers the green light. Their fracas made the man and doll on the grate seem all the more extraordinary. Traffic inched forward. She scanned the adjacent park for a child the Barbie could possibly belong to. Taking in a discarded jacket, tattered fast-food wrappings strewn over grass flattened here and worn there from what Marjorie imagined to be other bodies, her eyes came back, finally, to the doll. Her car idled beside the grate. She could see this was no carelessly discarded plaything. Barbie's long blonde hair was carefully arranged; she lay perfectly parallel to the man.

The doll smiled her enduring smile, her pert face empty, a reflection of the cloudless sky above her. The man, dressed in a worn muddy black overcoat and black knit hat, was as dark as the doll was light. The difference between them made him seem responsible for the doll's emptiness. She felt the same inner churning she experienced each time she heard another of those horror stories about missing children. She was being silly, this was a doll, not a child. And they were a man and a doll, not a couple. Dolls were for children—that must be the root of her discomfort.

Her own girls had played with Barbies, and she had enjoyed making the many outfits her daughters needed in their play. She remembered an evening dress cut from one of her old scarves, wrapping bits of chiffon around the long arms, measuring the skirt to cover the ridiculous rangy legs. The doll's dress suddenly lifted, ruffles tossed by a rush of subterranean air. The fluttering pink material reminded Marjorie of the cherry blossoms swaying about the Tidal Basin, of viewing the sky through the delicate haze of their flowering branches.

She was there just yesterday with her garden club. People—some with

259

cameras, others with small children—promenaded around the circumference, observing spring beauty in an ordered, civilized fashion. Only now did she realize why the experience had been so enjoyable. At the Tidal Basin there were none of the homeless that had taken over the rest of capital. Unwashed, their movements hindered by many seasons' worth of clothes, they lurched through crowds, mumbling to themselves, yelling, begging, sometimes lunging at passersby. They huddled by the entrances to office buildings, hunkered down on park benches, relieved themselves—although no one could blame them for that—in alleys and on the plantings in small parks like this one.

Once she allowed herself to see them, she discovered them everywhere. They were even in the park by the Arlington Metro stop near the restaurant where she and Burt went for Vietnamese. A retired army colonel who had last served in what he described as the Indo-Chinese theater, Burt had his own ideas about the problem.

"Work camps," he would bark in his no-nonsense military voice, pulling back his shoulders as they passed the men lounged on the cannons that flanked a statue of a local World War II hero. "Six months service, room and board, severance pay, job placement." He would take her arm, smartly escorting her through the entrance of the Golden Bee, as though the problem of homelessness was so simple it might very well be solved before they emerged from dinner.

There was a sharp rap on the driver's window. Stomach plummeting, Marjorie turned to look at a man holding out a large plastic coffee cup. He gave the cup a desperate shake, setting off the coins inside. Dirt covered his hand, compacted black beneath his nails. Just this morning she had planted pansies. Kneading the tender root filaments locked in neat black squares of soil, she'd watched, fascinated, as her own skin took on this same darkness, the boundaries between hers and the natural world suddenly blurred. A connection to plants was one thing, the idea of some relationship to this man was utterly frightening.

She moved her right hand to the lock button on her console, pretended to give her attention to the traffic light. Hadn't Burt warned her about keeping her doors locked when she drove downtown?

"You could help, lady, you know you could." The man's voice echoed off the glass, polite, reasonable. He held the cup to the window again, this time tipping it toward her as if he was offering her something. Gripping the wheel, she fought back an unexpected sensation of shame.

Out of the corner of her eye, she watched him move on to the next car. Her fingers relaxed their hold on the wheel. The moist circle of breath he had left on her window shrank, then disappeared. The light turned green and the driver behind her, anxious to escape the panhandler, rolled forward, nudging her into the intersection. She turned to glance one last time at the heating vent, but found her view blocked by the ring of shopping carts.

You could help, lady, you know you could. The man's words echoed through her head. She could remember when beggars sold things—pencils, apples—going about their business like everyone else. What did men like this expect? And what did they do with the money? She remembered Burt telling her how the men along this particular corridor, the island between the Watergate and K Street, begged in shifts, pooling the money they collected during the day to rent a motel room at night.

"Don't you think somebody that clever could figure out how to get a job?" Burt had demanded, tossing aside the metro section of the *Washington Post* in disgust.

Drawing a comfortable blank, she went back to her reading. But now she pictured Barbie perched on a battered dresser pocked with cigarette burns, smiling out over a room filled with the slumped, defeated bodies of men. Still shaken, she managed to find a parking space on one of the residential streets bordering M Street. Walking five blocks to the salon, she crossed once to avoid passing a man wearing a sign made from a cardboard box that simply said "Hungry."

She ducked into the salon, gratefully inhaling the orchard smells of shampoos and treatments. Ramon glanced up from the head of another client.

"You're late," he clucked, caught up in the heavily scheduled drama of his working clients.

Making what she hoped were apologetic sounds, Marjorie followed the shampoo girl to the back of the salon, slid the white smock the girl handed her over her dress. She stared at the featureless blue ceiling. Ramon claimed that the homogenized blue was to the eye what white noise is to the ear. Instead of relaxing her, the unremitting color made her think of Barbie gazing at the sky above the heating grate.

The shampoo girl draped a towel over Marjorie's wet head, another around her shoulders, led her to the empty chair beside Ramon. Punishing her tardiness, he went on fussing with a blonde woman who was obviously done. Marjorie watched him preen, murmur in the woman's ear. She thought of telling him about her experience. But the last time she confided in Ramon, about her girls not coming home for Christmas, she had ended up blonde.

"You need a change, M, something rejuvenating," he'd said, leading her to the colorist. "Feel good about how you look and everything else will fall into place."

"What does it mean, Ramon," she practiced saying to herself, watching him tease a strand of the woman's hair first back, then forward, "a man asleep on the street with a doll?" She thought of herself and Burt lying in their king-size bed, his presence a comfort, his hardy breathing the gauge and measure for her own. Was the doll a stand-in for a wife, a fantasy?

"That's enough, Ramon," the woman he was tending snapped. "I'll be late for my daughter's piano recital as it is."

Marjorie thought of her own daughters' recitals. She'd spent the hours just before their performances bathing them, curling their hair, pressing their dresses, polishing their shoes, each act filled with pride, purpose. A whirl of proms and parties followed upon the heels of the recitals. Ten years had come and gone since the youngest left home, leaving Marjorie with an aimlessness that had solidified like an arterial blockage.

"Empty nest," Burt had boomed at her, his big voice unstoppable in the newly lifeless house. "Better come on out to the links with me." But she failed miserably at golf, her ball either veering off the fairway into the trees or stubbornly refusing to do more than inch its way toward the green.

"You're just not connecting, Marjorie," Burt had offered.

An experiment with ethnic cooking was squelched early by Burt's lack of gastronomic adventure.

"What's that smell?" he'd asked suspiciously, coming in from a round of golf to a kitchen redolent of cardamom and coriander. After taking bites of her green curry and *pilau*, he refused to even try the *galub jamun* she'd worked on for days. Following her cue, he held one of the walnut-sized balls of milky dough perfumed with roses and saffron to his nose.

"I can't. It'd be like gargling with perfume," he said apologetically, tossing the sweetmeats into the beautiful shallow dish she'd chosen to serve them in.

Unsuccessful attempts at Italian and Chinese followed. She couldn't begin to think about Vietnamese; Burt knew the food too well. She went back to cooking the same dinners she had prepared all their married life: roast beef on Sundays, macaroni and cheese on Mondays, on and on until they were back to roast beef again. After eating these familiar meals on their appointed nights, they would retire to the den and the TV. Burt rolled through the channels, unaware that this might mean he too was looking for something more.

She sat beside him, staring beyond the flickering images, the suspicion that she could be doing something with herself a blight over all her evenings. What that something was continued to elude her. Her friends, also freed of childrearing, were going back to school, taking up painting, dancing. One even worked in a food co-op. But she'd never been what Burt called a starter. Her father had chosen her college, and then Burt, a senior and captain of the football team, had chosen her in her sophomore year. The children appeared of their own accord. And her garden, like the children, was simply there, needing tending.

"So, what are we up to today?" Ramon asked, one hand absently lifting her hair away from her head, the other hesitating over a selection of combs on the Lucite counter.

"Oh, I don't know. What about cutting a little here?" She pointed to a perceived wobble in the precise line of hair above her left ear. She intentionally chose styles that required maintenance. Her latest look was a geometric cut that Ramon snipped and reordered weekly. She watched him comb through her hair, turn a critical eye on each angle of her head. She was surprised to hear herself ask the question: "What would you think about me doing something for the homeless? Getting involved." The words felt brittle in her mouth.

She saw herself years earlier, a volunteer on picture day at her children's elementary school. Her task was to escort students from their classrooms to the auditorium, but she hadn't known what was expected of her. Should she should chat, offer to hold their hands? In the end she had walked stiffly beside them, a silent monitor.

Ramon gave the black plastic cape a serious snap, draped it over her smock.

"What are we talking about here? Fund-raising? Nobody wants to part with their money these days. I see it every day, women foregoing haircuts, letting themselves go—"

"I was thinking maybe of something a little more hands-on," she interrupted weakly.

Ramon paused. Two vertical lines formed between his eyebrows; his hand smoothed the dark hair contained by pomade. It was the same look he wore whenever she asked him for a new style.

"There are always the shelters, the clinics, but really, M, that seems a little extreme for you." He combed a lock of hair over her cheek, pulled back to study her reflection. "Maybe you're just tired of being blonde."

"No, it's not that. I just haven't found my niche." She realized she'd been saying the same thing to Ramon for 10 years. Perhaps this urge to do something for the homeless was no bigger or more pressing than any of her other whims. She was about to ask him what he thought her niche was, a question she'd never thought to ask, when a woman about her own age strode up.

"Not tonight, Ramon. Don't tell me you're behind. I've got a house to show in 40 minutes." Beyond her suit and heels, the woman looked too frazzled to give much thought to her appearance. "I almost canceled again," she added, a small practiced threat in her voice.

"Maybe I thought you would." Ramon gave the cord to the blow dryer a yank, cordoning off himself and Marjorie. He signaled a shampoo girl sweeping up shorn hair on the other side of the salon. "Don't worry," he said when she continued to stand her ground, "you'll be there."

"These days," he murmured above the hum of the blow dryer, as the woman stomped off after the shampoo girl, "everybody, everybody's a big shot." He gave Marjorie's shoulder a reassuring pat. "Of course, I'm not talking about you, darling."

Burt spread a spoonful of mint jelly over his sliced leg of lamb, examined her from beneath his substantial eyebrows. "Don't be ridiculous. The last thing those men need is a handout."

"I just can't get that picture out of my mind. The doll—"

"Why does it have to mean anything?" Burt asked, breaking in. "He's crazy, how about that?"

She studied the careful stitching in the monogram on her napkin. Why had she spoken about this to Burt? The familiar small regret of telling him too much came quietly over her.

"You're letting this thing bother you. Look at your plate, you've barely touched your dinner."

Marjorie saw her girls—Annie, the youngest, sitting across from her in her old seat, Emily at her left. Annie rearranges the food on her plate, slowly transferring the green peas behind the hillock of mashed potatoes. Marjorie and Annie exchange small conspiring smiles while Emily distracts Burt with a story about school. Emily's face is impassive but beneath the table her foot bounces against Marjorie's. Where had it gone, this bond with her daughters that reached on through them to life itself?

"There are children out there, Burt," she said, the memory of her daughters bringing her back to the doll. Burt pushed his dinner aside, unfinished. She couldn't remember the last time she'd said anything that had the power to interfere with his appetite. "Children," she added for good measure, "living on the street."

"Those men don't·have children; they're disturbed." He pushed his chair back suddenly, as though he was annoyed with her for making him repeat himself and strode into the den. Marjorie heard the familiar click of the remote, a snip of a basketball game followed by a commercial for beer.

"Aren't you coming in?" Burt called, the edge in his voice implying he expected her to. The remote clicked again.

There was the high-pitched sound of bullets flying, tires screaming. For the first time in 32 years of marriage, she left the table as he did, as though someone was coming right along behind her to take care of things. Upstairs, she passed through their bedroom, took the steps to the attic. She waved her hand through the dry still air, caught the string dangling from the single bulb. The vaulted space flashed in a sudden turquoise brightness. The attic had been the girls' playroom in the years between babyhood and adolescence. She came here once in the fall and again in the spring to bring down that season's clothes, but the color continued to surprise her.

She moved to the side of the room that still held their toys, dropped to her knees to fit under the sloped roof. She pushed aside a miniature pink range and refrigerator, maneuvered boxes into the light, turned them to read her faded handwriting: "Cowgirl Costumes," "baby dolls," "bake sets," "Barbies." After Annie left for college, Marjorie spent the better part of that first year sorting through the girls' closets, the basement, the attic—discarding, donating, grouping, labeling, packing away. She'd liked the purposeful feel of making decisions, of organizing. Whole months went by unnoticed with her too busy to wonder how to spend her day.

She could remember the moment when she put away the last box, the emptiness she had held off stepping right up to claim her. She'd thought of her mother after her father passed on, filling box after box with his things to give to Goodwill, never breaking down once until the loaded truck pulled away from the curb. Yes, it was just as much a death, the children's leaving.

She pulled out a box marked "snapshots," took out the manila envelope marked "Christmas." Dressed in matching flannel nightgowns, Annie and Emily stood in front of the tree, holding identical blonde Barbies. In another snapshot, the dolls were posed between them against an opened black patent leather Barbie carrying case. In still another, the girls sat on the floor, knees angled inward, dolls seated before them, all of them—girls and Barbies—waving like beauty queens on a Christmas parade float.

Burt's footsteps sounded across the living room, stopped stunned beside the dining room table. There was a large moment of silence and then a great clinking of silver, the sharp rattle of plates being stacked. She felt herself go tense as she did each time she crossed him. She began to hurry as she always did in the wake of his anger. The box marked "Barbies" opened easily. Her hands flew downward through the dolls' many outfits, nails catching on zippers, buttons, a bit of netting, a piece of lace. A doll emerged, smiling the same smile she remembered from this afternoon.

She dug through the box again, bringing out the black patent carrying case embossed with Barbie's profile and the doll's name in candy-pink swirling script. Inside was another doll, wearing the same party dress as the Barbie on the grate. She sat back on her heels, overwhelmed by coincidence. She dropped the photograph of the dolls standing under the tree into the carrying case, added a handful of clothes.

Burt climbed the stairs to the second floor. The Barbie carrying case under her arm, she bolted down to the bedroom, almost colliding with him.

"What are you doing, running around the house with your purse at this hour?"

Marjorie stepped backwards, tightening her grip on the doll case. She pushed the decorated side against her ribs.

"I won't be long. I promised Bea I'd drop off my book on bulbs. She needs it to prepare for the club's garden tour next week." She hadn't known she planned on going out. Amazing, how easily the lie tumbled out of her mouth, how quickly Bea's name—the one friend outside the circle of acquaintances she shared with Burt—came to her. She held her breath as Burt set the alarm on the clock radio, took off his watch. Anything he might be poised to say about the dishes was thrown off by her unexpected departure. His familiar movements seemed exaggerated, slowed, as if he was giving himself time to second-guess her.

"Now?" she heard him say above the blood pumping through her head. "It's almost eight."

"I meant to do it today when I went in to get my hair done, but I forgot to take the book down from the attic." The lie had taken on a strange veracity, one she could endlessly embroider with detail. She could clearly see the bulbs Bea might talk about—bluebells, lily of the valley, freesia. If pressed, she would be able to describe them down to foliage and fragrance. Burt waved the newspaper he took from the nightstand in her direction, headed back downstairs to the den.

"Call me when you get there."

"Burt, I'm just running in and out." She heard him pause on the landing.

"I missed a good game, you know, washing those dishes."

Marjorie stuck her head out the bedroom door, forced a bright smile.

"Why thank you, Burt."

"All right, then." He slapped the newspaper against the side of his leg. "Be sure you lock your doors."

"Thank you, Burt," Marjorie mimicked herself on the way out to the car. What was she thanking him for? Staring at her reflection in the rearview mirror, she took the Barbie from its case, held its face beside her own. "Thank you, Burt," she said, the set of her mouth a perfect likeness of Barbie's. Heading downtown, she retraced her route from this afternoon. The vent at the edge of the park was empty, the shopping carts were gone.

The man who had approached her on her way to the hairdresser stood at the intersection, his cup replaced by a large white plastic container. A few drivers opened their windows, dropped in change; meter money, she imagined, quarters for tolls. She ran her hand over the slick surface of the doll's carrying case on the seat beside her. The light changed. She turned right, made the U turn that would bring her alongside the beggar. She watched him work his way down the median, waiting for the moment when he would approach her. Her nervousness reminded her of her tension at the Communion rail; anticipating the sudden presence of the priest, the abrupt placement of the Host on her tongue.

This line of chance Communicants, what need did they hold in common in this unanticipated act of sharing? Suddenly it was her turn. The homeless man held his container to the window, starting slightly when he realized the glass was already lowered. There was nothing in this face marked by prolonged suffering to say he remembered the earlier moment between them. Marjorie managed to find her voice. "This is for you." She thrust the doll case through the window. The light changed and the traffic rolled forward, urging Marjorie to do the same.

Trembling, she adjusted the rearview mirror, saw him open the case, upend it. The Barbie and clothes tumbled out. The photograph, caught by a breeze, flitted along the median, dropped into the gutter. She watched him shake the case, expecting more, until he fell outside the frame.

SUCCESS OF A CYPRESS

Reed Venrick

ONE

Years ago, when I first bought an acre
of this wetland marsh, I planted a bald
cypress sapling—that was when
the trunk was no wider than my finger.
Close to the marshy edge, planted it
a few yards up from the cattails, hoping
it would grow quickly, as I was devoid
of shade, and I wanted to muse my days,
gazing over ponds and lily pads in fine,
feathered cypress shade

without sunburn, for what other shade
grows in wetlands anyway? But no,
this cypress tree was stubborn—
perhaps invasive grassy roots inhibited it
down under, so in the dry seasons I hauled

many buckets of water up from the pond
in back of my pickup truck, trying to give
that tree a boost, even fertilized it with

15-2-15 and watched it hardly grow more
when the summer rains soaked its roots.
A botanist at the arboretum suggested
I prune it back to force a burst of growth,
so I pruned, I watered, I fertilized, I mulched
but the soil was sandy—infertile, as they say.
Only grudgingly it grew so slowly that once
my neighbor remarked—should cut it down
and plant a palm near our pond to give a
tropical ambiance,

"And besides, palms are evergreen,
not like those deciduous cypress trees
that for months in winter go bare looking
like they've gone dead."

Many seasons passed, many times I despaired
to think my lone cypress would ever give shade,
but it was following its own schedule,
and after a decade or so, it finally took off

and shot out limbs longer than my arm in just one spring,
and the green branches soon expanded
and filled out to create an aesthetic
arrowhead shape—pointing up to clouds.

Now the canopy is finally wide enough
and shades enough to park my car
and picnic table in summer, and a place
to contemplate stars that circle lily pad ponds.

TWO

From this cypress tree, which the hands
of the gods shaped into a giant arrowhead
in the wetland side, for all my effort,
I have not made a dime or a dollar.

Nor have I impressed my gated-community neighbors
for my botanical awareness when they drive by
in their status cars and wave, one yelling out once—
"You should have planted palms!" Adding,
"Trees are best left to our yard workers up from Mexico!"

And the real estate agents who crowd my
mailbox when the economy inflates, hasten to add
that the value of my land won't change a dime because
a bald cypress beauty has grown to sixty feet.
Better to bring in fill dirt from the coast—
make a white, sandy beach, then you'll get top dollar.

Because the EPA maps show this marshland sits
inside the lines of the dreaded 100-year flood plain,

where you can hardly pull a building permit, even
if you build a stilt house for flooding hurricanes—not
without high insurance, and even to mow here is a no,
for which the water management agency will fine you 5k if anyone complains.

I ask the friendly sandhill cranes sometimes:
by growing this cypress tree, what is my reward?
Musing in the breezy shade, sipping on oxidized
water—no, my picture does not appear
in the society pages of the local newspaper,
which leads me to assume my social status
has not increased by planting an awesome cypress tree.

But the pond birds do seem impressed by my cypress tree—
they light on limbs and blare out their morning tunes,
and the mourning doves later lament and welcome
a night in the tree, and the red-winged blackbirds
with their buzzing tones, nest in spring inside the limbs,
and the anhinga and herons perch on top
of my lone cypress—now the highest pond-point.

I will say this from a shady retrospect:
I have changed my wetland acre with
the addition of a tree to gain the comfort
of a fine feathered canopy here on the edge
of a Florida marsh; I have nurtured a cypress

tree to grow into a monument with a trunk
the size of my waist.

And for a man of my balding age, I must say,
resting here today, down under a tree of this
shady size and tailored aesthetic shape,
this is no small fruit.

FOR WHOM I SING

Teresa Willis

Response to "Where I Live," a breast cancer oratorio

I have never had cancer but
I tell you it lurks
quiet and real

Twice my cells have been deemed
Questionable
Twice there has been cutting and burning
of flesh containing said cells
Twice the tears of relief flowed
at the utterance of the word
"Benign"

Today I look at the nine strong females
of the next two generations
The high-risk spawn
of a single-breasted matriarch
Stats in *Glamour* magazine tell me
two will surely fall prey,
NPR numbers say maybe even three
One will die, by Oprah's count

Oprah says at least one of us
will die.

But today we frolic
enfolded with our men
We cook and laugh
Seemingly free

Our breasts sagging, full, or showing promise
Our ovaries active, fallow, or wholly ignored
Our cervixes pinkish-grey guards to the ebb and the flow
of our uninterrupted womanhood
Still Momma takes her cancer pill
One a day for 20 years
and fashions clever homemade prosthetics
from discarded shoulder pads
that don't quite conceal her endearing asymmetry.

I have never had cancer but
I tell you it lurks
quiet and real

I sing for my Momma
I sing for my sisters
I sing for my nieces
I sing for myself.

HOME

"*Home should be an anchor, a port in the storm, a refuge, a happy place to dwell, a place where we are loved and where we can love.*"

—Marvin J. Ashton

QUEEN CITY

Margo Taft Stever

Coming back to Cincinnati,
a wayward soul looking for a sign, I see the city
stretching out like a foresworn promise.

The thing next to cleanliness—Cincinnati—
host to Proctor & Gamble, the Smut Buster,
Skyline Chili. I now return like a blind man

inhabiting a woman's body, an alien
within an alien, hopelessly lost, sensing Cincinnati
will always be foreign. The city will always catapult me

to a childhood endlessly spinning
out of control. Cincinnati, oh city of fountains,
squares, new buildings I will never recognize,

what is your plan? Returning to the once great
Queen City, riverboat town, gateway to the south, I find
ghosts of the underground railroad, Mapplethorpe, race

riots, boycotts. Cincinnati, where crows combed the outlying

fields in awful stillness, and dogs barked as if they alone
knew their voices echoed for miles down hollows,
where are you now? Where is the Cincinnati filled
with concrete strength, suppressed love, waiting breath,
this city of my youth with everything opening, where smells

of spring meant daffodils covered whole hillsides
with yellow? City once called Porkopolis, where hordes of pigs
pushed pedestrians off streets, once trashed

by Frances Trollope, why am I coming back to you, land
restlessly stolen, abandoned in adolescent
despair, vanished island, lost promise of light?

JUST AS I AM

Laura Johnsrude

I stopped conversation cold in a Chicago restaurant when I described religious fervor to some new friends who were not, and had never been, churchgoers. In between sips of wine, my anecdotes led to what, exactly, "being saved" meant.

Had I been saved?

Well, yes, I had. When I was about 12 or so, on a church youth retreat to Umstead Park, after hours of guitar singing around a bonfire, I felt elevated, like I'd been chosen by the Spirit. There was hand-holding and swaying and praying and yearning and then my soul lifted up into the humid sky, and I felt shivery and radioactive, like I was emitting sparks and laser beams. "Like a spiritual orgasm."

The other three, perched on high stools around a tiny table in Francesca's, stared at me, open-mouthed.

My upbringing was Southern Baptist, the hellfire-and-damnation version, and I'm not likely to forget the details of those many hours in church, three to four days out of seven, throughout my childhood. Now, in my 50s, I go to an exercise class on Sunday mornings, which is a spiritual hour of a sort, but not at all what my parents intended, and I sometimes feel guilty, knowing what a disappointment my choice is for them. Although I miss the white Christmas candles and the silence after a prayer, I don't miss the numbing repetition, the distribution of shame, the discomfort of dissent.

There were lessons aplenty to absorb from the balcony of our small-town Southern Baptist church, where my family had a celestial view of the congregation—the heads of white people sitting in rows, lifting hymnals, shaking hands, shushing children, sliding over to let in a latecomer.

The sanctuary was about half full of the faithful and the balcony, less so. We sat up there because Daddy frequently fell asleep during the sermon and there were fewer people to notice. Once, at the end of the preacher's exhortation, he called on my Daddy to lead us in prayer. We elbowed down the pew, "Pray!" and Daddy stood right up and began, "Our heavenly Father . . ."

Too often for me, our service ran over the hour, culminating in a long invitational hymn. I particularly dreaded the revival weeks, when there were extra services, heavy with doom and dire warnings, with no expectation of early dismissal. Revival was for winning souls and the preacher worked up a hot-blooded delivery with lots of yelling and finger-wagging, urging us to the altar, as though the world was ending that night and we only had this one last chance to make good with the Lord. He beseeched us to find our way down the aisles and bend our knees to repent and rededicate our lives to God. By the time "Just as I Am, without One Plea" played on the organ, we'd already listened to biblical lessons about God's wrath and been assured that we were unclean, unworthy. We'd nodded at the neighbors, praised God, passed the offering plate, and stood for the Doxology. It seemed high time for an adjournment, followed by punch and those little daisy cookies that fit on your pinky—the ones with the round holes in the center.

But, we were just getting started. The gory part of the hymn, with all the blood and sacrificial allusions, droned on and on, sung over and over again, while the pastor stood, arms outstretched, like a shepherd calling his prodigal lambs. "But that thy blood was shed for thee, And that thou bidst me come to thee, O, Lamb of God, I come, I come. . . . "

I always stretched out "I come, I come" with a plaintive drawl, like a slow country music dirge, hoping that the song would end. Instead, we were on to the next verse as parishioners stepped out of pews. Sometimes, they trickled down to the front; sometimes, there was a wave lined up to be touched by the preacher, heads bowed, sweaty and warm with the glow of the Holy Ghost. The pastor, thin hair plastered down with oil and always frowning his disapproval, was buoyed by the flood. And the organist played on, "To Thee whose blood can cleanse each spot, O, Lamb of God, I come, I come. . . ."

My feet ached and I slouched and sat down but was prodded back up by my mother poking me in the back. I peeked around her to look at my brother and search for one of those tiny pencils so we could play Dots on the bulletin. I was inattentive, at that young age, to the message, which, many times, was only directed to the men, being "heads of the households" and all. If the preacher wasn't talking to me, it didn't seem that I needed to listen. And why did everyone need to troop down to the altar to talk to God? They all could ask God's forgiveness inside their heads, like I did.

When I was a teenager, there were a few times that I stepped into the aisle during the invitational. Feeling like a sinner, dirty and unworthy, hot blood suffused my face and I felt a tug in my heart grabbing me and forcing me to walk to the altar and whisper, "I want to rededicate my life to God," culminating in a shivery, sweaty, blessing percolating from my scalp to my toes. Similar to the feelings I could conjure up in my bedroom, but with a less attainable goal and a more public display.

We cycled through the verses, plodding along in a weary rhythm, until all the penitents were spent and glassy-eyed, and the pastor was left alone at the front, hands moist and well-wrung. The preacher raised one hand to the rafters, pinched his eyes closed tightly and tilted his head towards the ceiling, thanking the Lord for those of the flock who had been lost but now were found, and we stood stock still, frozen in place, until the booming release, "*Amen!*"

Those Sundays are far behind me, but when I drive to North Carolina to spend the weekend with Mom and Daddy, I bring nice pants and shoes and accompany them to their new, progressive church in Raleigh where a gay couple joined last year, where they sometimes house the homeless, where my Daddy works in a clothes closet, and my mother manages the library. I go to church out of respect for my good and kind parents so they can introduce me to their friends, and to give them hope that I might end up in heaven with them. Sunday morning at their church, where I'm only a visitor, is so familiar—the reds, blues, and yellows of stained glass reflected on the floor, the children in tiny versions of adult dress clothes, the bulletin on crème-colored cardstock paper with black type presenting the hymn numbers and the prayer list and the Wednesday night supper details and Bible classes, the dark burgundy balcony pews and the offering envelopes. Even the parishioners are familiar when they place a hand on my forearm and say, "We're so happy you've joined us."

My parents glow with pride that I, their firstborn, have joined them in their favorite place. They introduce me to passersby, "Laura, our oldest, is with us today. From Louisville." Kind faces smile at me, and say, "Well, aren't you lucky?" and I feel a pang of guilt that such a small effort, on my part, should be such a gift to my parents.

Their preacher speaks to everyone. His sermon is thoughtful without threatening us with retribution or damnation. There are cushions on the hard pews; a man in front of me takes notes; Daddy's eyes shut. The choir voices climb to the rafters, and we all stand automatically when the Doxology chords reverberate through the house, and I feel a warm glow in my chest, the words coming to me, unbidden.

"Praise God, from whom all blessings flow; Praise him all creatures here below . . ."

And then it's time for Communion, and I don't know what to do. I was raised to believe it a sin to partake if you have not repented or if you do not "believe," and I no longer believe in the God of the Baptist Church. Or, in any God who saves a select few and damns the rest. Maybe, I just don't believe in organized religion. Maybe God has nothing to do with organized religion.

When the plate is offered to me, I pass it without lifting a wafer or a thimble of grape juice, and I see my parents' eyes and know that they don't feel lucky anymore. They are afraid that I am lost.

If there is a devil, I am sure he is hooting and hollering, watching me come to my senses. I want to reverse time and choose the other path, grab the plate and gulp the body and the blood, wipe the hurt off my parents' faces. Because no self-righteous point of mine is worth the injury.

I have found the guilt in the sanctuary, just as I expected I would. But, this time, it's mine to claim, mine to absolve, just as I am.

THE LONG WAY

Sheryl Loeffler

Canton, Massillon.
  We called them out,
each city's sacred name—
    Mansfield, Wooster, Delaware, Columbus—
as we called out animals
    or license plates from other states,
to pass the backseat hours,
    traveling past fields,
past time,
    and over ancient hills,
where the Appalachians grew,
    where the slow glacier stopped.

No interstates for us
    as we retrace the journey decades later.
The dead will wait.
    The sky is sick,
green with heat and storm.
    Tornado weather—
words that we don't say.

Home

Lightning points a finger.
Thunder curses under its breath.
We stop to drink iced tea
in fast-food air conditioning
and wipe the misery
from our arms and faces
with wet paper towels.

One November,
I woke up from backseat sleep
to see the yellows, grays, and duns
of the stark Thanksgiving land,
the skeletal blacks of trees,
the cool evergreens,
dusted in frosting sugar.

Give us a moment
of that sweet coolness now!

And when we got there,
open arms—
My, how you've grown!—
and then benign neglect,
as they caught up and we explored
places we knew very well,
front stairs, back stairs,

pastries in a glass jar in the kitchen,
crystal rattling on glass shelves
when we ran
between the dining room and den—
Don't run, they said—
the dark green den
with peppermints in candy dishes.
We sucked them
as we sat on chairs too big for us
or pretended to study
the books on the bookshelves,
the prints on the walls,
the suffering, thorn-crowned Christ.

Lancaster, Circleville,
Chillicothe, Portsmouth—
the little cities sadder
as we traveled south.

Hanging Rock.
Beware of falling rocks.
We trained our cocked and loaded fingers
on the crag,
in case it tried to crush the car
or the log cabin
growing from the stone.

Home

Ironton.

Trains whistle in the distance
as they've always done.

We pull into the gravel driveway
and stop in front of the leaning garage.

Strawberries, grapevines, roses,
a maze, an arbor, a trellis—

memories of an old garden.
We open the back door

and drop our bags on the kitchen floor
and pour ourselves long, cold glasses of water

and take our places
at the wide, white dining room table.

This is what we've come to—

a room, full of presence. Empty.

Your glasses on the reading desk,

as if you'd be back soon.

RAIN

Yvonne Lovell

I.

It was a hurricane. Charlie. To be exact, a "tropical cyclone" that strengthened into a hurricane over the Eastern Caribbean Sea. It struck the island of Jamaica on August 17, 1951, leaving 154 people dead and 20,000 homeless. It was the deadliest of the Atlantic hurricane season and the worst hurricane disaster in the first half of the 20th century. I was three years old. It seems it rained forever. But I have no memory of time—not the day, not the hour of the day. I do remember it as if it were daytime, though it appeared somewhat dark outside. Not moody dark, nor scary dark, just dark from the lack of sunshine.

My earliest memory is being a small girl standing indoors looking out at the rain through a window high above her reach. But in my mind's eye, the rain seems more like translucent beads slowly gliding down the windowpanes. As I watch, it becomes like liquid glass coating the windows.

I was, by the time of the hurricane, living with my Aunt Matty. We lived in Matilda's Corner, now in the heart of the Liguanea suburban commercial district. I grew up hearing that Matilda's Corner got its name from my great-grand-aunt, Matilda Joseph. The house was old and there was a veranda. I cannot see where I slept, neither the kitchen, not the bathroom. But toilets would have been outside. I see a small house-like building toward the end of the lot, at the gateway.

I remember a thicket of tropical plants forming a fence through which no one could see. We didn't use this way to go out. We took another pathway leading toward an opening at the other end of our small parcel of land. This wasn't a literal gate either, but rather a visual cue that, beyond this point, only family was permitted to enter. The house was isolated at that far end of the dirt lane, which hid an explosion of tenements.

II.

My mother was beloved by Aunt Matty. The story goes, my mother was a talented student and an athlete. And she had an opinion. When my mother was a student, secondary education was costly and nearly out of reach for poor families. But my grandmother intended for my mother's education to continue—she would attend commercial school. But she was redirected into a program designed for jobs in the hotel industry. As my mother saw it, they chose only fair-skinned girls and those from families with money or influence. This practice left in place the very caste system education was designed to change. She was hurt. She told them so, and to her mother's horror, she was dismissed from the school. With no ready prospects in sight, my mother became restless. But soon she set her eyes on adventure, to follow the great migration of Jamaicans to the United Kingdom. I was four years old.

Arriving on December 6, 1952, my mother was among the first wave of British Caribbean people to emigrate to the UK after World War II. She sailed the same troop carrier, the *Empire Windrush*, that had been the first ship to arrive in Britain with Caribbean immigrants nearly four years earlier. Their arrival—a response to Britain's post-war reconstruction and recruitment for labor shortages in hospital services, met with resistance. Still it was a period of extraordinary population growth in England and the beginning of modern British multiracial society. These Caribbean migrants with their children and family members who followed, became known as the Windrush generation.

I knew nothing of my father. I was left in Jamaica in the care of my aunt, my mother's older sister who worked in a hotel too far away to get back home each night. I was still not quite school age, and Aunt Matty was the adult who cared for me. She was a woman without a husband or children; she had lost both—her son from rheumatic fever.

My own experience with malaria had, for years, disposed me to high fevers. When the fevers came, they would start with swollen glands, and I would shiver with cold in spite of the tropical weather. I can imagine her fright seeing me shiver in bed with a high fever. She would find a blanket or a chenille bedspread to wrap my thin body. Such a blanket or bedspread my mother would have sent to my aunt in a parcel from England. To my mother's generation, the parcels were a down payment on their debt for emigrating and leaving children behind. These remittances displayed the personal sacrifices they made. They filled the parcels with goodies to meet the high expectations of the entire family back home. But I imagine for my mother and great aunt, the parcels also were a reminder of a void—an unfulfilled desire to have their children with them.

III.

I hear silence in the rain. But rain is not silent. Still, I can hear its silence. It is uneasy. It pours over me, pointing to a memory deep within me. Rain haunts me. I find little solace in it—the way most people seem to have cozy memories of campfire treats or snuggling under the covers during a good heavy rain. No memories of fear of lightning and thunder as a child, of hiding under a bed; no, not me. And the notion of reading away a rainy day because it is a delightful experience is foreign to me. Rain is haunting because it is silent and with it comes the unknown, the unspoken. The rain is foreboding.

IV.

It didn't rain the day I emigrated from Jamaica to the United States, landing in Miami in October 1969. I strolled the airport halls looking at the store window displays during my long layover. The plane had arrived late—very late, and my connecting flight was to be rescheduled for Chicago and, then another onto Berrien Springs in Michigan the next morning. My enrollment at Andrews University was remarkable due to my detailed planning. But my preparation for migrating to a country had stopped at snow. I had never considered the nature of winter weather, the nuances of the temperature over months and weeks, even days, much less between seasons. The dreariness, the gray and shortened days.

I did not own a single item of warm clothing on my arrival—not a pair of corduroys or even sweaters. My entire wardrobe consisted of short-sleeved dresses of linen or cotton and very short in length. The sunny Miami October day gave me no hint of the cold or snow that awaited me on the ground at the Chicago O'Hare Airport. Still, a sudden awareness dawned on me; I should have a coat. I bought the short furry white coat in the Miami airport and soon found myself stroking its fuzziness. But it covered too little of me.

V.

Mack and I had just settled in for an evening in what I like to call his treehouse. Two, nearly three years had gone by since our last dinner together. My work and personal life had devolved into chaos and tumult. And I had returned to settle into a life I knew all too well—aloneness. It was dark as rain clouds seemed to hover. I could hear thunder in the distance. Before long, it grew louder and he said, "Let's go sit on the porch."

"Hmm, okay," I said reluctantly, and we headed to the front porch.

This porch was more like a deck because it was built from treated wood decking, cedar I think—the kind you assume would be used for the back of a house. This porch though, sat higher than any I've seen before. We went to the third level. An old pine tree had been left in place, with each porch level wrapping itself around it, completely enveloping the tree.

It was raining. The crackling sky signaled that lightning was coming. We didn't see it yet. It was pouring, the thunder roared and the crackling quickened as lightning dazzled across the sky. It was the kind of electrical storm common in Kentucky, the ones to which I could not grow accustomed. Lightning bolts always seemed to sizzle in place in the sky urging me to hide my eyes. We sat and watched till the mood of the thunder turned dark, but the sky intermittently brightened from the lightning, which now seemed dangerously close. We heeded its warning and contemplated retreating inside.

Mack told me he had always wanted to sit outside in the rain just to watch the lightning up close. But we had to be crazy! And yet this rainy night has stayed with me as much as my first. Maybe it was because, for once, I felt safe. I was not alone. A quiet picture of silence, this one, is a perspective changed. Rain never seemed more tranquil.

VI.

I live now in a place that gets no hurricanes, though tornadoes in the Ohio Valley bring their own fright. A place where, in a flash, whole buildings and cars might be swooped up off the ground and then splattered down in teensy pieces. I don't vacation in hurricane-prone places between July and November. But hurricanes still frighten me.

In the summer of 2017, the rain—a hurricane—once again battered my psyche. Hurricane Harvey made landfall in Houston, Texas, leaving destruction in its wake. The images of entire Houston families with children and animals rescued in boats from the desolation reminded me of the Great Flood. To me, Hurricane Harvey was the very coming alive of Genesis 7:18–19: "The waters prevailed and greatly increased on the earth, and the ark moved about on the surface of the waters." As the media images of the flood were beginning to recede, Hurricane Irma threatened close family members living in Florida.

Rain still overwhelms me. In my mind, I conflate Hurricane Harvey with the Great Flood. I watch the news and see the rain, how it expands the rivers and puffs up the sea, turning streets into open bays. I feel its uncontrollable nature in my gut and all around I see, I think, isolation.

VII.

I seldom think about the silence of that stormy day of my childhood. I don't remember anyone coming to see if we had washed away. I cannot remember hunger or discomfort, and as a child, I did not understand abandonment. But I believe that the brain protects us from pain in ways that we do not understand. And new research suggests that painful memories are much more likely to be accurate when we remember them years later.

Decades have gone by and I still think of the absent voices from my childhood—mother, father, aunt. But there is hollowness in my silence. And an aloneness lingers with me still. I watch images of the Texas storm wreckage, and I am immobilized. I don't know and cannot think what to do. Everywhere the voices are loud—warnings to evacuate, challenges to rescue operations, the unattended needs of those with little or no means. Now, I crave silence from the rain. I do not respond to cries of help for victims. There's a part of me that wants to, but I simply stand in place. I hear my inner self whispering, *Continue doing what you do, make your contribution where you are.* Still, I'm unsettled.

THE FIELDS

Tom Raithel

The gravel road that runs through these fields
can't deliver us from an oppressive sun.
Nor can the breeze that rustles the dry stalks
break the sweltering stillness.
The tractor in weeds. The wind-scoured barn.
The farmhouse dark in its grove.
Even the swelling sound of cicadas
can't blot out the deeper silence.

Our grandparents came from such fields.
The aunt who eloped with the preacher.
The uncle who raised six kids alone.
One cousin hanged himself in a barn;
his widow would sit whole nights
at the window. A half-sister served
as a nurse in the war;
her luggage came back to the farm without her.

We look down the line of telephone poles
that vanishes at the horizon.

We listen to insects rattle and whirr,

and we ask

how the love in the wood-frame farmhouse

could stave off the loneliness of these fields,

and whether the slant of summer's late light

ever softened the hard-edged shadows.

Previously published in *Tipton Poetry Journal* and *Dark Leaves, Strange Light* by Tom Raithel

WHAT I WANT

Selena G. Phillips

I want to be little again. I want to be a little girl. I want to be dropped off at Hedges Motel to stay with grandma and grandpa. Mostly grandpa. I want to run into Ralph's arms and be picked up like a feather. I want to run in the field and play in the woods. I want to watch the customers come in and ask for a room. I want to smell breakfast cooking in the '50s-style kitchen and watch the sleepyheads come in and eat. I want to have the all-important job of filling the cardboard containers of candy. We serve what Ralph likes best: Clark bars and taffy. I love to take the little pink-, blue-, and white-wrapped three-inch cylinders and neatly organize them into proper configurations. I want to take my old-fashioned blue bike and smartly survey my domain. I ride to the limits of the permissible boundary and back again. I only dangle briefly to the depths of my limits, for I do not want to be disobedient or cause dismay.

I want to be delighted with the daisies and dandelions and create a fresh bouquet of wildflowers and other colorful unwanted blooms. I want to have time to watch the ants and hear Ralph tell me how important each one's life is and that we should never kill anything . . . even ants.

I want to marvel at the earth.

I want to marvel at the earth and what it does and does not do but most at what it does . . . if we let it.

I want to take a blanket and spread it out and plop myself on my back. I want to look up at the immense sky, the blues, and clouds. I want to watch the clouds create figures in my imagination, and I want to watch the wind take those figures and transform them into something else that I recognize.

I want to think about . . . nothing.

I want to wonder . . . about everything.

I want to spend a day like time doesn't matter. I want to forget that time is configured beyond get up, play, eat, sleep, and repeat. I want a day to last so long and to be full of so many nonsensical activities that it seems to never end. I want my companions to be the vast emptiness of everything and the tiny fullness of nothing. I want my light to be the sun, my carpet the grass, my companion the creek, and the trees my walls.

I want to be told "Tonight is *Petticoat Junction*." And that simple statement brings a smile and the knowledge that we will have treats and laugh. No matter that I don't understand much of the plot, not that there was much of a plot. But the show will bring a simple life, pretty girls, and a couple of laughs. We sit in the cafeteria on wooden chairs. A stranger may join us. He will be oblivious and won't stay. He will not have the power to burst the bubble of contentment. The *Beverly Hillbillies* and *Green Acres* are our other favorite shows. It doesn't matter that I don't get these either. But the adults do, and it makes them laugh. I want them to laugh. It makes me happy.

In the winter, I want to sneak back to the pond behind the evergreens. I step gingerly around the newly frozen water. When I discover it is solid, I will kick and glide as I pretend to have ice skates and perform the latest Peggy Fleming maneuver. If I only had skates, I too could be in the Olympics.

I want to be called for supper. I want to run in and be pleasantly surprised by the menu. I want to be famished from playing outside in the warm and bright sunshine.

At night, I want Ralph to give me the little blue and pink plastic figurine that used to be atop a music box I never saw. I doubt that Ralph saw it either. I think he found the ballerina and thought it would be a good toy for me. He was right. I want adults to always be right. I want to be able to ask the questions and be given reasonable explanations.

I want to be picked up after a day and night of adventure.

I want my mom and dad to pick me up in the 1963 ultra-sharp beige Ford Thunderbird. I want to see them slim and beautiful and striking as a couple. My mother looks like Sophia Loren, and my father is James Dean. I want them to be proud that I am theirs, that I am beautiful too, that others find me alluring. I want them to be satisfied with the world they are working toward building. I want us to drive away from Hedges to return to our tan and green Redman trailer, knowing that the world is perfect and that nothing can go wrong.

KNOWING THIS MUCH

Cynthia Rausch Allar

Uncut cord draws me to this old school, its iron fence
wrought of memories, edges rough with age.
At 17, I stood silent on a stage,
draped in a loose blue robe, borrowed garments
to play dress-up, barely swelling belly cinched
tight in a hidden girdle. A living prop,
beatific, for my high school glee club's
"Ave Maria." My pregnant Madonna incensed
gossip-eating parents who knew my secret
was out before I did. (Their Catholic-bred
sensibilities did not extend
to tolerance.) Some invisible sibilance
unwrapped me that last day like cellophane,
as they handed me my diploma beneath stained

glass. I walked out these doors, out Daddy's door,
unbalanced by a bag of borrowed clothes, steadied
by rebellion that was all mine. Our Lady's
Home for Infants hid girls who'd played dress-up before
they knew the rules, but I wouldn't hide anymore—

except my *bad example* from Daddy's new kids,
his new wife's words wrapped around my head
and throat, pulsing still. They cut the cord,
laid him on my belly. He wailed atop
the void he'd made. I reached to comfort him, cup
head and bottom in my hands' embrace, but my hands were
tied, cinched tight by hospital rules. Days later,
in the nursery, I held his long-lashed eyes with mine,
pink fists to my lips a moment, then left him behind.

A cousin took me in, since I couldn't go home
again. Our Lady's took him, a motherless child,
orphaned as I had been. My arms cradled
phantoms, mother-love haunting me to become
what I had lost, to refill the empty womb.
I pulled the dangling cord and took him back again.
His father came by once, that *no accident*
his friend kept shouting maybe keeping him
away. My welcome wore thready and thin,
since a brief boyfriend wore a needle in
his arm, my hands pulling the belt, cinching
it tight around his biceps, barbiturates leaking
from his eyes as he slept, like the child in the next room.
I took the borrowed baby clothes and the son

who was all mine and left again. That child
could fall asleep anywhere, since I'd taught him,
it seemed, how to wander in the womb.
At my sister's, we rested while we could,
not knowing where else this meandering would
lead us. Across the table, pinochle hand
splayed out in his hand, sat laughing the man
who would be all mine. Daddy, wife and kids
in the front pew, walked me down the aisle.
Our son spoke a language that sounded, for a while,
like the Latin I'd learned in that old brick school,
magna cum laude given, silent, in that hall,
the Virgin and some cherubs the only audience.
I'd walked out, but not away, as that wrought iron fence

snagged a thin thread, unraveling me now
for 30 years. Son and his sister grown and gone,
I fight to refill again an empty womb,
feeling my way, hands tracing back a cord somehow
still attached to 17. A girl who
sang, who spoke in borrowed tongues, a girl
who confined her heart to paper, shrinking her world
to a fine point to survive. Dressed up now
in skin that's all mine, I've come back to a school
next door to that other, already breaking rules
to make things happen. Following a thread,
pulling at cords to see where they might lead,
cupping in my hands these books, paper, and pen,
knowing this much, at least, was no accident.

FLY, OHIO, 2004: NEW OWNER UNEARTHS HUMAN REMAINS IN FRONT YARD

Colette Tennant

It was 1962, and a body lay buried
beneath my cousin's arbor.

Small, red grapes held
seeds like tiny bones.

Their fruit tasted sweeter
than old love.

A bobcat lived in the hills
behind the house.

She wailed at night—the only one
to mourn the man beneath the grass,

though the white moon sent dew

at midnight

to cover the grapes

with winy tears,

and the porch swing

cried with every circuit—

beneath

beneath.

MAD DOG WIND

Sheila Carter-Jones

I keep hearing that mad dog wind howl
through the valley, scratch at windows
of company store houses, rattle bone chimes
long empty of marrow. It is the sound of
my father's bedridden beg for air, the sanctified
preacher's mouthful of prayer.

It must have been the way wind's cool
wet hands bent the screen door back until it
creaked like lungs pressed against 40 years
of December ice.

A boxcar full of storm is headed this way.
Some old hooded coalminer hangs on, arms
wrapped around one slick neck, hugs the rail
until air sacs are rot with black disease.

It must have been the way the wind rattled
the screen door that makes me hear my father's
breath—a slow draw in, then out in steady release
of the pick and shovel life to machines that lend

a steady push-pull of air into cavities being eaten
by the creeping darkness of the coalmines.
Funny, how it all begins to come back to me, what
I didn't see. My father's aluminum lunch pail empty
on the shelf, gray work pants folded away, boots
scuffed and slashed with bituminous cuts. Scars that
proved skin over pain is never a pretty thing.

And funny, until now I hadn't noticed my father
had grown old, not even when months before he asked
to buy him a cane. Hadn't noticed the knee of his right leg
could hardly bend up the back steps. Just saw the smile
he worked his face so hard to make.

CAN YOU GO HOME AGAIN?

Charlotte Bowling Roth

Maybe.

I drive the familiar road home from Louisville to Pineville. The expressway, to the two-lane highway, watch the mountains rise in anticipation. My feelings are mixed. Some apprehension braided with some nostalgic yearning.

It is gone—that physical home. The one where I grew from adolescent to adult. Destroyed by fire, leaving only the concrete slab on which it stood for over 60 years.

Or is home a place? The small town cradled in the belly of the Pine Mountain range that I call home. Feels like I belong as I drive into the town to be inducted into the Pineville High School Hall of Fame. Not for doing anything famous. Just for being a cheerleader on one of the most winning football teams in the history of the small independent school. Pineville is a football town. Football stars—revered forever.

Being part of the ceremony was important to me mostly because I would reconnect with old high school chums that I hoped to recognize. It had been so many years.

I skipped the Friday night football game, and I can't say why, really.

I stand in my appointed position in the formation of five other cheerleaders facing the fan-packed bleachers behind a chain-link fence, leading cheers on the home side of the field, freezing my butt off. In front of me, on the opposite side, are old men leaning by their elbows, coaching, spitting 'baccer, shooting the shit, from the sidelines. Guys whose glory days have passed. Guys who spent many nights on this field under these lights, hurrayed by the crowds and cheerleaders. Their blood runs maroon and gold, Mountain Lion lifers. Recalling intercepting passes, running 10-, 20-, 60-yard touchdowns, kicking field goals, defeating the Yellow Jackets, Redhounds, and Bobcats.

Maybe I didn't go because I knew that the chain-link fence surrounding Samuels Field would be lined with old classmates.

If I went to the football game to be called onto the field at halftime, etiquette would require me to stop and talk to those old men. I would know them all by name. They would be the hot hunks, tight ends, quarterbacks, linemen I had cheered on all those years ago.

The problem? I would no longer see hot and sexy buff guys. I'd see the balding, wrinkled, snuff-dipping grandpas of today. I'd feel sorry for them because they hadn't aged well, and they had chosen to stay in this small, gossip-ridden six-block town that I love. They were stuck in the past. Most of them still believe Trump will bring back coal and the town will thrive once again.

My room at the lodge was rustic, clean, meagerly decorated with holes in the black-out shades. I was disappointed. As I child, I thought the lodge was upscale and fancy. The rich tourists stayed there.

I sat at table seven during the induction ceremony at the Pine Mountain Lodge, with friends and old classmates, wearing around my neck the fancy medallion with the old school pictured in the center, which hung from a maroon and gold lanyard. The medallion conjured memories of the good old days. Gone for years, our school structure has been replaced by a modern version.

At the end of the ceremony, I stood at the podium with the other cheerleaders and led the room chanting our Mountain Lion Fight Song: "We're loyal to you, Pineville High." Delighted at the *che-cha-rah-rah-rah* verse, where with fisted hands we instinctively outstretched our arms and finished the stanza with the arm movements of the 1970s' cheerleading squads. *Pineville High School rah, rah, rah.*

As I mingled my way back to table seven, I'll be damned if I didn't run into those old men who stood before me in my youthful days. The ones who stood on that fence line the night before. And I was right. All those old football players I supported had indeed become mostly bald, wrinkly faced grandpas. A couple sported their old jerseys and letter sweaters, though. When I hugged them, they were soft centered like the Pillsbury Doughboy.

And the reality I had desperately tried to avoid hit me center field. Knocked the wind out of me. Those guys were looking at me and thinking, Damn, she hasn't aged well. She is an old, spectacle-wearing, wrinkly, graying grandma.

Maybe it is better *not* to go home again. That way, you never have to admit how much you've changed.

HOW I CHEATED ON
THE BLACK SEA

Irene Sulyevich

December 1989. We are standing in line at a Moscow airport, waiting to be checked by customs officials. Our flight is in two hours, but we are not sure we are going to make it. The line is moving very slowly, and this is intentional. The customs officers want us to choose between missing a flight and leaving our valuables. Why? Because we are leaving the Soviet Union, and we are leaving for good. We have already lost a lot—our jobs, our friends, our homes, and most importantly, our beliefs, so what person in their right mind would care about a few things of sentimental value like an old watch that was passed from generation to generation in the family? What family? It will be broken forever.

The officers' plan works. We drop everything at the customs counter and rush to the gates. We can't afford to miss our flight. We fought so hard to be on that plane! And we make it. We crash into our seats and sigh with relief. We are fleeing the country in hopes of changing our life completely, to a life we know nothing about. And now, let me introduce my family: my husband, his mother, and my two-year-old son, Alex.

The plane takes off, and the cabin, full of people like us, explodes with applause. We are finally free! Little did we know what the road to that freedom would look like. Our first stop of the six-month journey to the United States was Vienna. Upon landing there, we became nobodies. We became the property of immigration agencies; our lives depended completely on them. They could deport us for any or no reason. We were placed in a communal apartment where families of five to six people shared the same room, and the only word we heard from the landlord was "stink." But we didn't complain. We were on our way to a bright future. I remember my trips to the meat market. We couldn't afford to buy good meat, so we discovered a place where leftovers from a butcher shop were sold. I remember going through that pitiful pile of meat debris, trying to find something that was worth paying for, when a woman at the counter slapped my hand. "Don't touch it, dirty swine!"

That was it. I was labeled a second-class citizen, someone people wanted to avoid, someone who could be accused of stealing food at the market. Who cares that I have always been an honest, law-abiding citizen? I am a thief! I discovered how easily the self-esteem of an immigrant can be ruined and how hard is it to restore. I carried that mentality throughout our six-month journey and brought it to the United States.

Luckily for us, in the states, we met great people like the Brenner family— volunteers who helped us feel respected again. I vividly remember the night they met us in the airport. They radiated positive vibes, kindness and openness—something I had been longing for for a long time. They had two teenage daughters who immediately took Alex under their wings. But let me tell you a little backstory first.

I grew up by the Black Sea, where I would go to bed at night thrilled about my morning dive into its emerald waves, willing to give everything for another chance to be embraced by its mighty power. It was like being with a dream lover: you would never know what to expect; he would always surprise you but never disappoint you and never bore you, leaving you wanting more and more. That's why, when I first came to Louisville after an exhausting 24-hour overseas flight, my only question to a cab driver was, "Where do you swim here?" He looked at me in his rearview mirror, smiling, and said with a strong foreign accent, "In the bathtub, ma'am." I thought he was teasing me.

"You have a large river. Don't you have any beaches?"

He looked at me again, but this time he decided not to bother himself with answering. The Brenners looked at me smiling. They knew that there was a surprise waiting for me. We arrived at our apartment complex late at night, so my search for a beach was interrupted for a few hours.

The morning sun brought an answer along with the deepest frustration: a large crowded pool was winking at me just outside my balcony: "Did you bring your surfboard?"

What? No emerald waves, no iodine smell of seaweed, no baking in the sandy powder under a gentle, Mediterranean-like sun, no breezy romantic evening at beachside restaurants? Oh well, we could travel to Florida when we could afford it. After all, that is not a reason to be frustrated. I had bigger fish to fry. I clenched my teeth and focused on other things in my life— my son, my career, my professional development. I was trying to forget my sea the way you would try to forget your old boyfriend: you don't want to see anything that would remind you of him, but at the same time, you are craving just a glimpse of his life. What is he doing now? How does he look? Does he have a girlfriend?

And sure enough, the opportunity presented itself on one hot day in September. We had been looking for a house for a couple of years by then, and this house was the last one on our list. Exhausted and sweaty, we came out to the patio by the pool. The owner's family was sitting around the pool, relaxing in their beach lounges. I don't remember what they looked like. I was mesmerized by the color of the water. It was not just one color. It was a giant jewelry box filled with emeralds, sapphires, amethysts, and ambers threaded on a golden chain of the afternoon sunlight. I couldn't believe my eyes. I squinted and opened them again. *I want this necklace now! I want to wear it each and every day regardless of my outfit. Please wrap this house up for me.*

Since then, my life has taken a completely new turn. I had met my new lover, who slightly resembled my old one. He was a little older, wrinkles crossed his forehead, and his grayish hair had gotten thinner. But his touch is still the same. Once I jump into the water, he embraces me with his strong and gentle hands and carries me through the clouds of crystal splashes, flying with me to the top of the blue mountains, dropping me at the peak only to pick me up again just in time for another flight. I know I am safe in his hands. I turn to him when I am happy and when I am sad, when I need advice or when I am just homesick.

Sorry I cheated on you, my dear Black Sea! Will we ever meet again?

POTATO SALAD

Colette Tennant

And Aunt Leona's green beans
pressure-cooked with bacon and just
the right amount of sugar.
A watermelon, its cold green sides
sweating, red fruit glistening in the
moist Ohio sun.
Flowers and sweet grass
our only audience—and the faint,
comforting smell of cooking gas,
burn-off from a nearby oil well.
My mother organizes
food and people as if both
come to earth alphabetized.

Everyone is alive—
Uncle Buck with his chew of tobacco
and overalls blue as redemption,
Daddy in a new white shirt,
Papaw with my bashful cousin
sidling up to his safe lap,

Home

Nanny smiling her sweet smile
as she carries a pot of homemade
noodles to a picnic table already
heavy with food, and Uncle Paul
playing in a pickup baseball game
over by the cemetery where Mason
jars hold faded peonies.

Old hands outstretch, five fingers
flattened by the same motion
"She was only this tall"—
trying to hold
the lid down
on time?

FIVE DIRECTIONS
TO MY HOUSE

Karen George

After Juan Felipe Herrera's poem of the same title

1. Cross the river from Ohio to Kentucky. Use the Roebling Suspension Bridge. Notice the twin towers, rope cables, engraved date. 1867.

2. Reflect on borders. Ones you've crossed, ones remaining.

3. If mid-May, inhale the balm of locust blossoms. Pinch a honeysuckle trumpet, slide out the string until the pooled nectar appears. Lick it.

4. Round the lake where scruffy ducklings trail their mother.

5. Press a pulpy leaf of the live-forevers that lean against the limestone slab set on its thin edge—the silhouette of a halibut.

6. Bow to the gray wolf that guards my front door. Praise the wild ones.

Appeared on *Accents Publishing* blog for Lexington Poetry Month, June 2015

FANNY JUNE IS ASKED WHAT SHE REMEMBERS ABOUT HER MAMA

Kari Gunter-Seymour

I was maybe five years old. A doctor
came to the house. I remember his black bag,
mother in a straitjacket, panting.
A preacher's wife, a lot was expected of her.

Like me, she was raised to please.
Depending on the meds,
she carried out her duties,
moved church to church as obliged.

Uncle Bub told me, as a girl Mama
squirreled away coins, bought chewing gum,
gave a piece to a boy at school.
Her twin tattled. Grandfather lost control.

Now you tell me this woman who never
worked a day outside the home when married,

ran away, spent a year during WWII
working at an airplane factory in Detroit?
She was born in far western Kentucky,
passed when I was twelve, giving up
what was left of herself to the Maury soil
as we sang, rain dimpling the mound.

Hindsighted, I imagine her last thinning
breaths as liberating as those seams of perfectly
punched round-head rivets, a celebration
each time a B-17 rolled off her assembly line.

ENDINGS

"Live with intention. Walk to the edge. Listen hard. Practice wellness. Play with abandon. Laugh. Choose with no regret. Appreciate your friends. Continue to learn. Do what you love. Live as if this is all there is."

—Mary Anne Radmacher

AFTERWORD

Whenever we have discussed the Boom Project, people have spontaneously shared their own memories and experiences. We hope this anthology encourages readers to continue to reflect on the unique experiences of our generation. Not only are words a way to preserve the past, they foster greater understanding. Spoken or written, words offer new perspectives, courage to persevere, and the chance to leave a fingerprint and a punctuation mark. We hope you'll tell stories of influences that brought forth the person you are today or hope to become tomorrow.

Here are a few suggestions for your own Boom Project. First, take time to listen. You will be richer for doing so. Honor and respect those who left footprints to guide your way. Begin story circles among friends and colleagues; make it a theme for your next dinner party. Encourage schools and organizations to plan a "Bring a Boomer to . . ." program. Consider purchasing games or toys from a previous era for grandchildren.

We invite you to create additional events and methods to honor the past, celebrate the present, and inspire the future.

With our sincere appreciation,
Kimberly Garts Crum, Editor
Bonnie Omer Johnson, Editor

VIETNAM–A MEMORIAL

Bonnie Omer Johnson

We expected entries from veterans or loved ones of veterans of the Vietnam War, a defining event of our generation. We received none. Zero. However, we cannot in good conscience omit Vietnam entirely when the scars, nightmares, and addictions yet haunt our battle-scarred citizenry, thousands of miles and decades from combat. We wanted to give men and women a voice to share their experiences and to let American know how they survived—then and now.

We must not underestimate the toll of that war, or any war, on its generation.

Casualties stretch further than battlefields. Over three million people died in Southeast Asia, including almost 60,000 Americans. No data reveals the numbers of survivors who lost a purpose and a future. Over 300,000 men and women were wounded. More than half that number of homeless veterans in the United States must find a place to lay their heads each night. Before Vietnam, PTSD had no name.

We dedicate this page to all lives deeply affected by the Vietnam War, to those who died on the battlefield, and to those who didn't.

CONTRIBUTORS

(In alphabetical order by surname)

Cynthia Rausch Allar was born in Louisville, Kentucky, in 1955. Cynthia was one of three girls in an Irish-German Catholic family. She attended Catholic schools through high school but broke from the church at age 18. She married, had two children, and lived in various parts of the South and Midwest. At the age of 47, she was encouraged by a poet at the Indiana Writer's Conference to apply to a master's program at Spalding University in her hometown. There, Cynthia met the woman who would later become her wife, the wife her large Catholic family has embraced. Cynthia's work is most often about her family, friends, and their experiences.

Dianne Aprile was born in 1949 in Louisville, Kentucky, where she lived for 60 years and enjoyed a 30-year career as a journalist, during which she was part of a *Courier-Journal* team that won a staff Pulitzer Prize. She and her husband co-owned the Jazz Factory, a music venue with an urban vibe. In 2009, they (and their cats, Mr. Leo and the late-great Maya Papaya) moved to Seattle's East Side. Dianne is the author of four books. Excerpts from her memoir in progress have twice been nominated for the Pushcart Prize. Since 2001, Dianne has had the pleasure of teaching creative nonfiction as faculty for Spalding University's low-residency Master of Fine Arts in Writing program.

Joan E. Bauer was born in Long Beach, California, in 1947. She lived there through college, with stops in Berkeley and Washington DC, and has lived in

Pittsburgh since 1988. Her poetry demonstrates her interest in history as well as inspiration from other writers; some poems are based on true stories.

Sheila Carter-Jones was raised in Indianola, a small coal-mining town in Western Pennsylvania. Indianola was made up of ethnic pockets, each with a distinct nickname. Sheila lived in the place nicknamed Colored Town, adjacent to Peanut Heaven and Russian Town. When the coal mine closed in 1960, the African American men and women went to work for rich white people nearby. Sheila attended school in that affluent area and was offered a full scholarship to Carnegie-Mellon University. She taught at public schools and universities in Pittsburgh for many years. Her featured works are memory-tributes to the men and women in her hometown. Sheila's poetry manuscript, *Three Birds Deep*, won the 2012 Naomi Long Madgett Book Award, judged by Elizabeth Alexander.

Kimberly Garts Crum, born in 1955 in Richmond, Virginia, is the coeditor of *The Boom Project*. She has often lived near rivers, including the James, Rhine, Thames, Mississippi, and Iowa. In 1986, she and her husband adopted Louisville, a charming city that does not know whether it is midwestern or southern. Kim has her MSW (University of Iowa) and her MFA (Spalding University). She teaches memoir and personal essay writing at her Shape & Flow writing studio, located in a repurposed slaughterhouse, its incoming streets often flooded when the Ohio River tops its banks. She is working on a segmented memoir titled *Slouching toward Self-Actualization*.

Diane Cruze has lived in Louisville since her birth in 1955. Her featured piece, "Independence Day," remembers a childhood experience within a racist culture. The Fourth of July picnic is the first time she recalls being told by her parents that she was forbidden from playing with black children. It was a rule she always resented. As Diane came of age, she rejected the racism that permeated the world around her. Today, 58 years after this memory, Louisville's Olmstead Park System, along the Ohio River, invites people of all incomes and ethnic groups to concerts, festivals, and fireworks, especially on the Fourth of July. Diane is the director of Louisville's Women Who Write.

Joan Dubay lives in Louisville. Recently, she and her husband visited the historic site of the 1969 Woodstock Festival, Max Yasgur's dairy farm. The museum returned her to a time in her youth, preparing to enter her first year of college. She could never have imagined that the horrific experience of the Kent State massacre would close out her freshman year. This was a defining moment in the life of this boomer. It framed her political involvement and social justice outlook for the rest of her life. While writing her featured piece, "What Are We Fighting For?" Joan contacted Country Joe, receiving permission to feature the lyric from his iconic Vietnam protest song.

Nancy Genevieve, née Steinhauser, was born in Paducah, Kentucky, in 1947. Her family's history intertwines with the town's—her father and his father were born and buried there; her great-grandfather and his father are also buried there. Nancy originated and directed Murray State University's first writing center and taught at Trigg County High School where her students researched, wrote, and published six volumes of local history, titled *Echoes*. She also chaired Kentucky's first Rails-to-Trails Project in Cadiz. Even though Nancy moved to Illinois in 1990 and to Massachusetts in 2005, her family life, academic life, and writings, notably her *NYX* poetry trilogy, embrace her western Kentucky roots in attitude, language, images, and values.

Karen George was born in 1952. She has lived in many Northern Kentucky towns, never more than a half hour from the Ohio River. She grew up hearing stories about walking and driving cars on the frozen river. The 1937 flood reached the second floor of her grandfather's dry cleaners on 12th Street in Covington, Kentucky. Much of her life is, and always has been, crossing borders from Kentucky to Ohio and back. The Ohio River is braided tightly into her history. It even enters her dreams.

Joseph Glynn was born in Carbondale, Illinois, in 1961. Joseph has a bachelor's degree from Northern Illinois University, as well as master's degrees from Illinois State University and Indiana University in Bloomington, and a paralegal certificate from Roosevelt University in Chicago. He now works as a cartographic technician at the National Processing Center of the United States Census Bureau in Jeffersonville, Indiana. In his spare time, Joseph writes. He has his own blog that houses his literary creations and personal interests. As a "tail-end boomer," Joseph hopes that he and his fellow comrades will one day gain the respect they deserve.

Kari Gunter-Seymour was born in 1955 in Warren, Ohio, but has lived all her knowing life in the countryside of Athens County, where she currently serves as poet laureate. She came of age as the true nature of the Vietnam War was becoming known to the American public and has been *fired up* ever since. Many boomers were raised by parents who served during WWII, including moms who became Rosie the Riveters. Women did not have the kind of choices we have today concerning career and birth control—especially rural women. So little was known about mental illness, or how to treat it. Kari was compelled to put down a version of a story she overheard.

Roger Hart was born in Columbus, Ohio, in 1948 and lived in numerous small towns in Ohio for 60 years. He sometimes accompanied his father, who sold soap and floor wax for Rose Chemical, to schools and courthouses in towns along the Ohio side of the river. A retired teacher, Roger relocated with his wife to Iowa although he still remains a Buckeye at heart. His piece is based on an actual event, the collapse of the Silver Bridge in December 1967, a tragedy that is well remembered. As the story suggests, Roger found the love of his life and two very large Newfoundland dogs.

Suzanne Hartman was born in Louisville, Kentucky, in 1946. A graduate of the University of Louisville and Spalding University, Suzanne has lived most of her 72 years in Louisville. She is a psychologist. Suzanne loves her city in the Ohio River Valley, but also believes that racism still penetrates the South's soul. She has grown to realize the depth of injustice towards her black brothers and sisters. Her essay grew out of her effort to try to understand racism in the context of her white privilege.

Lennie Hay was born in 1950 in Minot, North Dakota—an unlikely place for a Chinese American child to enter the world. She has lived in Louisville, Kentucky, since 1972 and now spends half the year in Indian Shores, Florida. Lenora's poems are memoir-driven. At 18, she was a young woman with a passion for the presidential campaign. Fifty years ago, she watched her black-and-white portable television and cried. On a late August evening in 1968, she watched in disbelief as the Chicago police clubbed protestors gathered at the Democratic Party's National Convention. She remained hopeful that the country could change, the Vietnam War could end, that race relations would improve, and poverty would decrease.

Ginny Horton credits Crosby Stills Nash and Young, Cream, and Simon and Garfunkel for everything that happened in her life since 1968. She blames the family TV for Kent State, the draft, and Nixon. When her big brother got drafted, Ginny got his record player. In the suburbs of Cincinnati, music spoke to something deep in her. She did not know any protestors or hippies, but felt her world changing as she memorized the lyrics of the generation, her imagination going around with the movement of the turntable. Ginny is a retired advertising creative director. Her work has appeared in *Travelers' Tales: The Best Women's Travel Writing.*

Bonnie Omer Johnson, coeditor of *The Boom Project*, was born in Lansing, Michigan, in 1948, but moved to Kentucky before her first birthday. She claims to have river water running through her veins, having lived more years than not on the Ohio River, but also in cities along the Missouri, the James, and the St. Johns Rivers. Since receiving her MFA at Spalding University in her mid-50s, she has taught at Keiser University, Owensboro (Kentucky) Community and Technical College, and Bellarmine University in Louisville, Kentucky. A lifelong curiosity propels her into old age, where she loves and laughs, reads and writes with ever more delight as she looks forward to overtime in the game of life. "Hair Peace" is memoir that recalls a single vanity and practices of mid-20th century haircare.

Laura Johnsrude was born in 1961, in Winston-Salem, North Carolina. She spent four years during her pediatric residency in Cincinnati. Her family has lived in Prospect, Kentucky, for the last 17 years. Laura is sure she lives in the Ohio River Valley since she and her son walk over the river on the Big Four Bridge whenever he is home. And she can hear the foghorns from her own backyard. Laura has published in *Hippocampus, The Spectacle,* and *Bellevue Literary Review*. In her anthology piece, Laura explores her childhood and its religious complexities.

Don Krieger lives and works in Pittsburgh as a researcher, where he earns his living trying to understand and treat head injuries. In his creative writing, he tries to express ideas with unambiguous clarity and intensity. His poetry has appeared online in *Tuck* and *Uppagus* magazines, and in print in *Hanging Loose, Neurology,* and *Persian Sugar in English Tea* (volumes 1 and 3) in both English and Farsi.

John Limeberry was born in 1962 in Louisville, Kentucky, and spent most of his childhood years in southern Indiana. He spent much of the turbulent '60s in a cocoon of safety and innocence. He suspects that many of the younger boomer generation can relate to this experience, which is reflected in his piece. Through the use of notable markers such as television, church, and family, John attempts to articulate what it was like to be an actual child of the '60s.

Sheryl Loeffler was born in Canton, Ohio, in 1949. Her mother's family came from Ironton, Ohio, where Ohio meets Kentucky and West Virginia. Although Sheryl has never had a permanent home in Ironton, she and her family spent virtually every holiday there. She is now a Canadian writer and musician. Her poetry has been published in literary magazines in Canada, the United States, the United Kingdom, Austria, and Japan. In April 2005, she moved to Malta, at the heart of the Mediterranean Sea. In May 2014, *A Land in the Storytelling Sea*, her book of poems, prose poems, and photographs, born in Malta, was published by FARAXA Publishing, Rabat, Malta. In 2015, she was elected to membership in the League of Canadian Poets.

Yvonne Lovell immigrated to the United States from Jamaica at the age of 21. She is an immigrant from a long line of immigrants and likes to refer to herself as a citizen of the world. Her sisters are citizens of Canada, her cousins are British, and the rest of her family has adopted the United States of America. In this moment in the United States, Yvonne believes immigrants are struggling to understand, how did they get here? What did they do to insult our host? How did they cross that line between welcome and unwelcome? Or did they? Yvonne explores her memories and understandings in the world to grapple with these complicated questions she believes she and her fellow immigrants must ask themselves.

Colleen McCormick was the editorial assistant for *The Boom Project*. She was born and raised in the suburbs of Philadelphia, Pennsylvania, and is a recent graduate of the University of Louisville. Her featured work, "A Woman's World," salutes all women, past, present, and future, who defy stereotypes.

Colleen is the daughter of a baby boomer, a representative of the millennial generation, whose assistance enabled *The Boom Project* to select stories and poems with universal appeal. She hopes this is one of many meaningful literary contributions.

Wendy McVicker was born in eastern Pennsylvania, during a snowstorm in January 1951. She grew up in the anodyne suburbs of Philadelphia, all smooth surfaces and roiling underneath. Since 1985, she has been a resident of Athens, Ohio, pursuing the life of a rogue and teaching poet, while raising two sons and practicing karate. Wendy's poems reflect growing up female in that suburban world of the 1950s, trying desperately to figure out who she was in a world that sought tirelessly to wear her down.

Robert Miltner was born in Cleveland, Ohio, in 1949. Robert attended the College of Steubenville and Xavier University of Cincinnati for his undergraduate education. These years were important to his transition from childhood and adolescence, shaping his emerging identity and personal and cultural growth. Robert believes he can truly identify with Langston Hughes when he said, "I've known rivers," and as such, his understanding of his life and times, "has grown deep like the rivers." Even more, Robert knows this revelation is also reflected in his writing about his generation and the Ohio River Valley.

Mary Lou Northern was born in 1947 in Louisville. Though she has lived elsewhere, she always returned home. One of eight children, among them an artist, a potter, a poet, and a musician, she received her MFA from Spalding

University. Her work has appeared in *Redbook, Orion,* and elsewhere. Three of her plays have been produced. When she was a girl, her father taught her to skip stones across water at the 4th Street wharf of the Ohio River. It was the first time she saw a rat and a steamboat. Her father lived in her childhood home until he was 89 years old. One February day, he went out in the snow, he believed, to help the sheriff secure a prisoner. A gas and electric man brought him home. Her father's dignity and love inspired Simon and Eleanor's story in her featured piece.

Kenneth Parsons was born in 1953 in Ashland, Kentucky. He is a graduate of the University of Kentucky, Marshall University, and the University of Illinois in Urbana-Champaign. Kenneth has taught English in colleges and universities in the United States, China, Japan, and South Korea, where his poems have also appeared. His poetry chapbook, *Window Shadow Mirror,* was published by Pudding House press. His novel *Our Mad Brother Villon,* was published by Little Feather Books (2015). Kenneth now lives in Goyang City, South Korea, and he recently retired from teaching English as a foreign language at SeoKyeong University in Seoul.

Selene G. Phillips (Wabigonikewikwe) is a member of the Lac du Flambeau Band of Lake Superior Ojibwe nation. She was born on February 8, 1959, in Rhinelander, Wisconsin, in a hospital just off her reservation. It was five days after "the day the music died" when Buddy Holly, Ritchie Valens, and J. P. "The Big Bopper" Richardson died in a plane crash during a tour that began in Milwaukee. Her job as an assistant professor in the department of communication brought her to the Ohio River and the University of

Louisville, where she teaches and researches writing and Native American studies. She lives in Floyds Knobs, Indiana.

Laura Power was born and raised in western Pennsylvania. She studied civil engineering at Carnegie Mellon University in Pittsburgh. That's where Laura met her college-days boyfriend, and, more importantly, learned to drive his damask-red MG Midget. Mastering a stick shift seemed a more formidable skill then than all the nerdy measuring, calculating, and analyzing required at school. A few years later, Laura began a brief, but beautiful, relationship with her own MG Midget. Following a career as a corporate drone, Laura now writes as a hobby and sometimes as a freelancer.

Michael "Mick" Puckett was born in 1951 in Louisville, Kentucky. He spent his youth in the woods and along streams and rivers. In his work life, Mick recorded albums for local musicians in his studio, Real to Reel Recording, as well as on-location music festivals for NPR. He worked with artists John Hartford, Jean Ritchie, John Jacob Niles, and Lily May Ledford. Later on, he taught middle school science and biology at Indiana University Southeast. In his retirement, Mick is a volunteer for Raptor Rehabilitation of Kentucky, where he treats owls, hawks, falcons, eagles, and vultures and releases them back into the wild. His piece, featured here, is a memory of Vietnam War protests just after the Kent State massacre.

Tom Raithel was born in Milwaukee, Wisconsin, in 1951. He graduated with a bachelor's degree and a master's degree from the University of Wisconsin-Milwaukee and worked as a journalist for several newspapers in the Midwest, including 20 years with the Evansville (Indiana) *Courier and Press*. He currently resides in Evansville. He believes his poems show a respect for the natural environment of the Ohio River Valley as well as the industrial-urban and rural environment that often encroaches upon it.

Linda Neal Reising was born in Miami, Oklahoma, in 1955, but has been a resident of Poseyville, Indiana, since 1980. When her daughter was in high school, she became obsessed with James Dean. Every time Linda opened the door to her daughter's room, she was face to face with a life-size cutout of the "Rebel." When Linda attended the Indiana Writing Project at Ball State University, she was given the assignment to write a what-if story. Immediately, she thought of James Dean. What if he didn't really die in a car accident? What would he do? Where would he go? Poseyville seemed liked the perfect place for him to hide.

Charlotte Bowling Roth, whose roots run deep into the mountains of Eastern Kentucky, raised a family in and has enjoyed her Louisville, Kentucky, home since she was a young mother. But occasionally her eyes turn toward home, the small town of Pineville, Kentucky, where the first-grader who sits at the desk behind you is the same young man who stands beside you in the line at graduation. These memories are the basis for her featured piece which wonders, "Can You Go Home Again?"

Mike Schneider was born in 1946 in central Pennsylvania and has lived in Pittsburgh since the mid-1970s. His father and maternal grandfather served in the European theater during WWII, a family experience that he feels has helped shape his life. He began writing poetry in the early 1970s, when he published an antiwar underground newspaper at an air force base in Ohio. Since then he's been a lawyer, grad student in literature, freelance writer, and science writer for 25 years at Carnegie Mellon University. Now *jubilado* (Spanish for "retired"), he's published poems in many journals, along with two chapbooks, most recently *How Many Faces Do You Have?*, which won the 2017 Robert Phillips Prize from Texas Review Press.

E. G. Silverman was born in 1953 in Pittsburgh and lived there until he departed for college in 1971. One of his first jobs was working at Bageland on Murray Avenue in Squirrel Hill during the summer after his junior year of high school. "Bagel Macher," which first appeared in *Pangolin Papers*, is loosely based on that experience, although the characters and events are fictional. Silverman's fiction has appeared in many literary journals, and he's been a finalist for several awards for his short story collections and novels.

Margo Taft Stever was born in 1950, in Cincinnati, Ohio, where she lived until she attended Harvard to study poetry and visual studies. When she left Cincinnati, Margo thought that she might never return. Now, she visits as often as possible to revel in the study of the city's history. Margo has an MFA in poetry from Sarah Lawrence College. She founded the Hudson Valley Writers Center and is the founding editor of Slapering Hol Press in Sleepy Hollow, New York. Many of her poems reflect her Ohio roots and her childhood memories. In 2019, her second full-length poetry collection, *Cracked Piano*, will be published by CavanKerry Press and her fourth chapbook, *Ghost Moose*, will be published by Kattywompus Press.

Dana Stewart was born in 1962, in Louisville, Kentucky. By the time she was six, she was critically ill, diagnosed with a rare lifelong condition, dermatomyositis, which left her using a wheelchair by the time she turned 13. Dana spent much of her time in the hospital reading. From there, her love of writing grew. Dana's featured work was inspired by her mother and grandmother, two avid readers who kept Dana occupied and never dwelt on what she was missing.

Irene Sulyevich was born in Odessa, Ukraine, in 1957, and immigrated to Louisville, Kentucky, in 1990. Writing has been her passion since she was 10 years old. However, the rigorous censorship of the Soviet era made publication unrealistic. These days, her writing is an escape from a job as an IT systems analyst. She writes personal essays and short stories inspired by her multicultural experience. Her memoir piece in the anthology reflects her early experience, being parted from her beloved Black Sea.

Christine Telfer was born in Pittsburgh in 1964, nine months after the Kennedy assassination—the event that kicks off her poem. Growing up in the aftermath of that event, as a "late boomer," left her with a sense that there had been a time when the dream of a better, peaceful world was alive in hearts and minds. Her poem was inspired by a comment made in a poetry workshop after a poem about 9/11 was presented and reflects her search for an event that similarly shocked her generation. Christine served as a Peace Corps volunteer in Bulgaria (1991–1993) and has since made a living teaching English as a second language to immigrants.

Colette Tennant was born and raised in Columbus, Ohio. She spent much of her growing-up years in her mother's hometown, Fly, Ohio, right across the Ohio River from Sistersville, West Virginia. She grew to love the dear, hardworking people there. Even more, Colette knows it will always be an important part of who she is now.

Leslie Smith Townsend is a marriage and family therapist who spends much of her free time writing. She believes that as a baby boomer female, it is easy to lose oneself amid the various roles of wife, mother, grandmother, employee, volunteer, etc. Writing is the way she calls herself back to her true self and sorts what really matters from what should be let go.

Judith Turner-Yamamoto lives in Cincinnati, Ohio. She searches for the profound and unexpected in the everyday and explores the constellation of emotion in the dynamics within family and community. Years ago, while living in Washington, DC, she drove by an underpass in Georgetown and saw a black man asleep on his back on a heating grate, a blonde Barbie doll clad in a red party dress clenched to his chest. For those few moments, the world fell away. When the traffic light changed, she knew she'd seen something singular that would find its way into her storytelling. And it has. Judith gave this experience to her protagonist, Marjorie, in the featured piece "Offering."

Reed Venrick was born in 1949 and received his PhD at Indiana University of Pennsylvania, near Pittsburgh. He usually sets his poems in a natural place or an international context, having lived in five countries during his career as a linguistics and grammar teacher before retiring to a family farm in Florida.

Yvonne Vissing, born in 1953, grew up in Jeffersonville, Indiana. Her stay-at-home mother hailed from a farm family and her father was a car businessman who became mayor. Her dad thought she should become a secretary, but her mom pushed to let her attend Indiana University Bloomington. Working on the *Belle of Louisville* became a way for Yvonne to help pay for college, and it afforded her a unique opportunity. She grew up on the river. A picture of the *Belle* hangs on her bedroom wall, and memories of the days of working on the river inspire her still.

Nancy Wick was born in 1947 in Butler, Pennsylvania, a conservative place and time where it was uncommon for women to work outside the house. Girls had to wear dresses to school and were required to take cooking, sewing, and home management in junior high. She arrived at college in the late 1960s, when second wave feminism had hit its stride and all the societal rules of Nancy's childhood were called into question. Those years, through Nancy's 20s and early 30s, shaped her consciousness and continue to inspire her writing. She now lives in Seattle.

Mark Williams was born in 1951 in Evansville, Indiana. After graduating with an English degree from Vanderbilt University in Nashville, he returned to Evansville where he sold real estate for many years. Now he writes. This story is the second part of Mark's five-part novella, *Shangri La*. On a World War II training run from Dyersburg, Tennessee, his father flew over the Ohio River and bombed the Evansville shipyards. "Bombs Away!" was inspired by that flight, as well as his father's bombardier pin and Mark and his wife, DeeGee's, cat Redbud, whose meow sounds like *now!*

Teresa Willis, born in 1960 in Louisville, Kentucky, had an authentically wonderful baby boomer childhood. As she aged, her gratitude for her upbringing crystallized as she realized how rare her family was. Fun, spiritual, intellectual, and life-loving, they still gather regularly despite her parents' passing years ago. Teresa's work is often informed by her family and their shared experience, as well as the letdown that the present day now seems in comparison. Teresa eventually returned to her native Louisville, where she now lives with her wife, Laura Shine, in comfortable proximity to her big sisters.

Sheri L. Wright is from Louisville, Kentucky. One of her earliest memories was being forced to use pink construction paper because that's what girls were supposed to do. In first grade, she hated pink and gender inequality, and has not changed her mind about either. A two-time Pushcart Prize nominee and a Kentucky Poet Laureate nominee, Sheri is the author of seven books of poetry. Her literary and visual work has appeared internationally. "Girls Room II" was first published in her book, *In the Hall of Specters* in 2018.

REPRINT
ACKNOWLEDGMENTS

(In order of appearance)

"The Ohio," by Tom Raithel, was previously published in the *Southern Poetry Review* and *Dark Leaves, Strange Light* (Finishing Line Press, 2015).

"In the Eye of the Storm," by Dianne Aprile, was published in *The Things We Don't Forget* (1994). Permission to reprint courtesy of the author, who published under Trout Lily Press (now defunct).

"As We Sleep in Our Cribs 1947," by Joan Bauer, was published in *Uppagus* literary journal.

"Mad Dog Wind," by Sheila Carter-Jones, was first published in Broadside Lotus Press. Permission to reprint courtesy of the author and Broadside Lotus Press.

"One More Time?" by Nancy Genevieve (née Steinhauser), was first published as "Baby Boomers" in *Daughter of Chaos* (NYX Series, Vol. II) at Nox Press.

"Ironing to WIBG 1965," by Wendy McVicker, was first published in the chapbook, *Sliced Dark*, a collaborative project with artist John McVicker (self-published).

"Red and Yellow, Black and White" was written and performed by Teresa Willis as part of a one-woman play, *Eenie Meanie*. It has not previously been published in print or online.

"Girls Room II," by Sheri L. Wright, previously appeared in her book, *In the Hall of Specters* (2018), published by Amazon Digital Services LLC.

"The Fields," by Tom Raithel, was previously published in the *Tipton Poetry Journal* and *Dark Leaves, Strange Light*.

"It Was So Italian of My Mother," by Joan E. Bauer, was published in the *Paterson Literary Review*.

"Wish You Were Here," by Karen George, was first published in *Swim Your Way Back* by (Dos Madres Press, 2014).

"Queen City," by Margo Stever, will be published in her book *Cracked Piano* (CavanKerry Press, 2019). Reprinted with permission of the Permissions Company on behalf of CavanKerry Press, www.cavankerrypress.org.

"Along Came a Spider," by Kimberly Garts Crum, was published in *The Louisville Review* (Spring 2016). Permission to reprint courtesy of the author and *The Louisville Review*.

"Five Directions to My House," by Karen George, was first published in the *Accents Publishing* blog (2015).